With the name of Allah, the All-Merciful, the Most-Merciful

Road of the Shepherds

Abu Muhammad, Qasim ibn Inayat Ali

British Library Cataloguing in Publication Data
A catalogue record of the book is available from the British Library.

Written by; Abu Muhammad, Qasim ibn Inayat Ali

Illustrated by; Ishaq Aamir Chowdhury and Masud Ameen

Edited by; Sheikh Ridwan Kajee, Sheikh Suleman Mall and Bint Inayat

Front Cover Design by; 'We, the People co.'

Published and Distributed by;
Jamiatul Ilm wal Huda
30 Moss Street
Blackburn
Lancashire
United Kingdom

Tel: 01254 673105
Web: www.jamiah.co.uk
E-mail: info@jamiah.co.uk

Also available from:
Quwwatul Islam Masjid
Email: info@quwwatulislam.org.uk

ISBN: 978-0-9556973-7-1

Printed by: Imak Ofset, Turkey

Life is short, though to me the road seems long.

Shaytaan ambushes the weak, so I must stay strong.

I must lighten my load, for a burden it will be,

when I reach the end of the road and my final abode I see.

- Abu Muhammad, Qasim ibn Inayat Ali -

لَقَدْ كَانَ لَكُمْ فِي رَسُولِ اللَّهِ أُسْوَةٌ حَسَنَةٌ لِمَنْ كَانَ يَرْجُو اللَّهَ وَالْيَوْمَ الْآخِرَ وَذَكَرَ اللَّهَ كَثِيرًا

"Indeed, for you, in the Messenger of Allah there is an excellent example, for him who hopes in Allah and the Last Day, and remembers Allah much."

- Qur'an 33:21 -

عن عبد الله ابن عمر رضي الله عنهما قال سمعت رسول الله صلى الله عليه وسلم يقول

كلكم راع و كلكم مسؤول عن رعيته والرجل راع في اهله وهو مسؤول عن رعيته والمرأة

راعية في بيت زوجها ومسؤولة عن رعيتها والخادم راع في مال سيده ومسؤول عن رعيته —

قال وحسبت ان قد قال — والرجل راع في مال أبيه ومسؤول عن رعيته وكلكم راع

ومسؤول عن رعيته

'It has been narrated from Abdullah the son of Umar (Allah be pleased with them), he said, "I heard the Messenger of Allah (Allah's peace and salutations be upon him) saying, "Each one of you is a shepherd, and every single one of you will asked with regards to his flock. And a man is a shepherd in his family and he will be asked with regards to his flock. A woman is a shepherdess in the house of her husband and she will be asked regarding her flock. And a servant is a shepherd in his master's wealth, and he will be asked with regards to his flock. – the narrator says and I recollect that he said – and a man is a shepherd in the wealth of his father, and he will be asked regarding his flock. And every single one of you is a shepherd and will be asked regarding his flock."'

-Narrated by Imam Bukhari (may Allah have mercy upon him) -

Can You Imagine the Euphoria ...

... of Ubay bin K`ab 🌼, when to him Rasulullah 🕌 did say

"Allah has commanded me, to you, Surah Bayyinah I should pray."

Ubay 🌼 was overwhelmed and exclaimed, "Did Allah name me to you?"

Oh how I wish Allah could have taken my name to Rasulullah 🕌 too.

... of Mu'adh bin Jabal 🌼; what went through his head?

When the following words to him by Rasulullah 🕌 were said,

"O Mu`adh ... I take an oath by Allah that I love you."

Oh how I wish he said those words to me too.

... of Abdullah ibn Abbas 🌼; a happier moment he could not have faced,

than the one in which by Rasulullah 🕌 he was embraced.

"O Allah, teach him the book," then Rasulullah 🕌 did pray.

Oh how I wish he embraced me too and those words for me he would say.

... of Sa`d ibn Abi Waqqas 🌼, when at Uhud, next to Rasulullah 🕌 he did stand,

whilst protecting Rasulullah 🕌 with bow and arrow at hand.

And Rasulullah 🕌 said, "Shoot Sa`d ... may my father and mother be sacrificed for you."

Oh how I wish I was stood there and he said those words to me too.

... of Ali ibn Abi Talib 🌼, when one of the forts of Khaybar would not fall.

To take the flag 'a man who loves Allah and His Rasul 🕌 and they love him,' Rasulullah 🕌 would call.

All the Sahabah wished for the flag but it was handed to Ali 🌼.

How I wish I could have been amongst them and wish it was handed to me.

... of Uthman ibn Affan 🌼, when the army for Tabuk needed to be prepared,

he donated copious amounts of wealth and between the Muslims it was shared.

Then Rasulullah 🕌 said, "Nothing Uthman does, will harm him after today."

Oh how I wish I too could have donated such and these words to me he would say.

... of Aa`isha bint Abi Bakr 🙵; she would have been elated,

when without any hesitation, her name Rasulullah 🙵 stated,

when he was asked, "Who amongst the people is most beloved to you?"

Oh how I wish I could have been amongst those he named too.

... of Abu Bakr as-Siddeeq 🙵, the man who was always by Rasulullah's 🙵 side,

when to the Sahabah, the following words Rasulullah 🙵 did confide.

"If I was to take a friend ... I would have taken Abu Bakr as a friend."

Oh how I wish I too could have accompanied him to the end.

... of Bilal ibn Rabah 🙵, when to him Rasulullah 🙵 conferred,

that the sound of his footsteps in front of him in Jannah he heard.

Rasulullah 🙵 asked, "In Islam what action is it that gives you most hope that you do?"

Oh how I wish I can also be one who is honoured by walking alongside him too.

... of Umar ibn al-Khattab 🙵, when to Rasulullah 🙵 he did go,

and asked permission to enter, from the Sahabah who guarded his door.

"Give him permission and give him glad tidings of Jannah," Rasulullah 🙵 said.

Oh how I wish that once it could have been me to knock on the door instead.

... of Abdullah bin Salam 🙵, for Islam his high position he forsook,

when at him Rasulullah 🙵 told people to look,

if a man from the people of Jannah they wanted to see.

Oh how I wish he could have said the same regarding me.

... of Abu Bakr 🙵, when by Rasulullah 🙵 he was told,

that his name from all the gates of Jannah will be called,

and the first of the followers to enter it he will be.

Oh how I wish for all the gates of Jannah to call for me.

... of Abu Ubaydah 🙵, when to the people of Najran a man Rasulullah 🙵 said he would send,

who is indeed trustworthy; by this Abu Ubaydah 🙵 was the man he did intend.

As the trustworthy one of this Ummah he became well-known.

Oh how I wish in the company of Rasulullah 🙵 I too was born.

... of Abd ur-Rahman ibn Awf ؓ, when during the expedition of Tabuk, the prayer he did lead.

Rasulullah ﷺ arrived late and behind him his salaah he did read.

Though to lead anyone in prayer worthy I am not,

oh how I wish to pray behind Rasulullah ﷺ I chance I got.

... of Salman the Persian ؓ, who was not from the Muhajir or Ansaar men,

when to dig the trench around Madinah, Rasulullah ﷺ was splitting them into groups of ten.

"Salman belongs to us, he is from the Ahl ul-Bayt," Rasulullah ﷺ said to Salman ؓ, who had no family.

Oh how I wish in his household he too could have included me.

... of all of the Sahabah, who saw Rasulullah ﷺ day and night.

who travelled with him and alongside him they did fight,

who prayed salaah behind him five times a day.

and heard from his blessed mouth the wonderful words he did say.

... of mine, if to me Rasulullah ﷺ was to say,

on the day that I meet him; on Judgement Day,

greeting me with open arms when me he does see,

'You are my brother, who didn't see me but believed in me.'

Contents

Introduction.. 17

Arabia before Rasulullah's ﷺ Birth 30

The Year of the Elephant 32

From Birth to Marriage 34

From Marriage to Apostleship 39

The First Revelation.. 42

Preaching Begins.. 44

Persecution 47

The Migration to Abyssinia... 50

Hamzah ﷺ Accepts Islam... 53

Umar ﷺ Accepts Islam 54

The Boycott.. 56

The Year of Grief.. 58

The Night Journey – al-Isra.. 61

The Ascension - al-Mi'raaj... 63

The Pledge 67

The Hijrah – Migration to Madinah................................ 69

In Madinah 77

The Battle of Badr 80

The Aftermath of Badr 87

Banu Qaynuqa Break the Treaty 90

The Battle of Uhud.. 92

The Aftermath of Uhud..102

The Betrayal at ar-Raji..104

Massacre at Ma'una..107

The Expulsion of Banu Nadeer...109

Badr – The Appointment 111

The Reconnaissance of Doumat ul-Jandal.........................112

The Invasion of the Confederates 113

The Siege of Banu Qurayzah 121

The Treaty of Hudaybiyah 124

The Manifest Victory 129

Propagating Islam..131

The Conquest of Khaybar 132

The Expedition of Rags..136

The Umrah..139

The Campaign of Mu'tah 141

The Conquest of Makkah 144

The Battle of Hunayn...148

The Campaign of Ta'if 150

Hawazin Accept Islam..152

The Expedition of Tabuk..155

The Farewell Pilgrimage 159

The Final Journey 161

Alternation of the Day and Night 164

The Wayfarer 166

With Difficulty Comes Ease 168

The Seeker of Knowledge..170

Selfless...172

An Innocent Child..174

The Kindler of Peace..176

The Lone Child...178

The Stray Child..180

What Am I?...182

Man's Last Thoughts...184

Definitions...186

Endnotes..205

Introduction

الحمد لله نحمده ونستعينه من يهده الله فلا مضل له ومن يضلل فلا هادي له واشهد ان لا اله الا الله وحده لا شريك له وان محمدا عبده ورسوله اما بعد

"All praise belongs solely to Allah. We praise Him and seek His assistance only. Whomsoever He guides none shall ever mislead him, and for whomsoever misguidance He decrees, none shall ever be able to guide him. I bear witness that there is no deity but Allah and I bear witness that Muhammad ﷺ is the servant and messenger of Allah."

All praise is for Allah, the Lord of the worlds, who has saved us from the darkness of disbelief and has illuminated our hearts with the light of imaan. Glorified is ar-Rahman who sent the messengers, the best of men, to guide humanity towards the path of righteousness which leads to the pleasure of the Creator. Greatest is ar-Rahim, whose complete and all-encompassing mercy did not leave mankind blind in the depths of darkness, in which they would have been ignorant of the enlightened road to salvation. Majestic is as-Saboor, who gives mankind opportunity after opportunity to turn to Him in repentance despite mankind's persistent disobedience and sinning. Magnanimous is al-Gaffar, who anticipates the moment his servants turn to Him in repentance and eagerly forgives all the sins of the sinners.

May His salutations be on His beloved Rasul ﷺ, who is a mercy to mankind and an exemplary role model who laboured tirelessly throughout his life to ensure each individual from his Ummah can reach man's ultimate goal. He who constantly worried and made concern about how every person can be saved from the flaming fires of Hell and be granted entry into the gardens of eternal bliss. I pray that each of our actions is done solely for the pleasure of Almighty Allah.

All the messengers made an effort on their people to change their convictions, priorities and concerns, from acquiring the world to acquiring the hereafter, from earning wealth to earning everlasting rewards through good deeds and from relying on the creation to relying on the Creator. Numerous examples of these can be found in the life of the Messenger ﷺ.

Umar ibn al-Khattab ؓ says that once I entered into a room in which the Messenger of Allah ﷺ was lying on date leaf matting. There was nothing between him and the bedding, the pattern of the matting could be seen imprinted on his body. He was leaning on a pillow which was a leather bag filled with the bark of the date-palm.

I said, "O Messenger of Allah! Pray that Allah may grant ample provisions for your Ummah. Verily the Persians and the Romans have been given ample provisions whereas they do not worship Allah."

The Messenger ﷺ said; "Are you falling in this matter, O ibn al-Khattab? They are a nation to whom their share of good has been hastened for them in the life of the world."

In another narration it is mentioned that the Messenger of Allah ﷺ said, "Does it not please you that for them is the world and for us is the hereafter?"

Look at the bedding of the most beloved of Allah; if this was his bedding we can imagine the simplicity and poverty in which he spent his life. If success was in this world then Allah would have given Rasulullah ﷺ the world, but true success lies in the hereafter. Though Umar's ؓ request was due to being unable to bear seeing Rasulullah ﷺ in such a state look at how Rasulullah ﷺ directs Umar's ؓ inclination of the temporary world to the eternal hereafter.

When the Muslims had conquered Khaybar and its booty and wealth became their lot, the companions of Rasulullah ﷺ began to buy and sell what had become their share. One man came to the Messenger ﷺ and said to him, "O Rasulullah, I made such profit that nobody will have profited today as much as I have profited."

Rasulullah ﷺ enquired, "How much did you profit?"

The man answered, "I continued buying and selling until I made a profit of three hundred ooqiyah of silver."

Rasulullah ﷺ said, *"I will inform you of something better than that in terms of profit."*

The man asked, *"What is that? O Rasulullah!"*

Rasulullah ﷺ replied, *"Two rakaats (of nafl) after (obligatory) prayers."*

Three hundred ooqiyah of silver is approximately 36.74 kg. The Sahabi seemed to have shown partiality towards the wealth of the world, upon which Rasulullah ﷺ immediately reminded him of the everlasting reward of good deeds in the hereafter. We need to make an effort on our imaan such that two rakaats of salaah become more valuable to us than all the riches of the world.

The hands of Fatimah ﷺ, the youngest daughter of Rasulullah ﷺ, were pained due to grinding and the heavy burden of the daily household chores. News reached her that some prisoners had come into the possession of Rasulullah ﷺ. She went to him (to ask for a prisoner as a servant) but did not find him there. She met Aa'isha ﷺ, the wife of Rasulullah ﷺ, and informed Aa'isha ﷺ of her situation.

When Rasulullah ﷺ arrived, Aa'isha ﷺ informed him of the coming of Fatimah ﷺ. Rasulullah ﷺ went to Fatimah ﷺ and her husband, Ali ﷺ.

They had retired to their bed, upon his arrival they made haste to get up, but Rasulullah ﷺ told them to stay in their place. He sat between them such that the coldness of his feet could be felt on her chest, then said, *"Should I not inform you both of something better than that which you asked for? When you retire to your bed say 'Allahu-akbar' thirty four times, and 'Subhana-Allah' thirty three times and 'Alhamdu-lillah' thirty three times. This is better for you both than a servant."*

Again the Rasul of Allah ﷺ is making an effort on the imaan of the Muslims. Rather than relying on the aid of the creation in our household chores he taught us that by reciting the above mentioned Tasbih ul-Fatimah one should seek the aid of the Creator, who will remove the tiredness of the day and help one in their daily tasks.

Three years after receiving revelation, Rasulullah ﷺ was ordered by Allah to openly preach Islam by commanding him to warn his near relatives. So Rasulullah ﷺ ascended Mount Safa and called out, "Ya Sabahah!" This was a call used to get people's attention of an imminent threat or attack. The people of Makkah became anxious and rushed towards Mount Safa and those who could not attend sent a representative.

Rasulullah ﷺ called his related tribes, "O Banu Abdul Muttalib, O Banu Fihr, O Banu Ka'b." He then asked, "Tell me, if I inform you that there is cavalry behind this mountain ready to charge at you, would you believe me to be true?"

All of them replied, "Yes!"

Rasulullah ﷺ said, "Thus I am a warner for you, of a severe punishment before it comes."

Abu Lahab retorted, "May you be perished forever. Did you call us only for this?" (In response to Abu Lahab's curse Allah revealed Surah al-Lahab, 'Perish the two hands of Abu Lahab and perish he.')

Ponder over the situation and demographics. Mount Safa is in the centre of Makkah, mere seconds away from the Ka'bah. It was the centre of paganism where all idolaters would flock for pilgrimage. It is one of the biggest cities in the Arabian Peninsula. It is surrounded by desert. For an army to have reached the centre of Makkah and be stationed behind Mount Safa without anyone noticing would be deemed impossible.

Firstly, an army that would attack Makkah would have to be significantly large as they are attacking a well-populated city. So the size of the army would not have gone unnoticed. Furthermore, Rasulullah ﷺ mentioned the army was mounted, so the clamour of the army and the horses would have been heard.

Similarly, the army would attack swiftly in order to take them by surprise. As Makkah is surrounded by desert, an army travelling at speed would have caused a lot of dust to rise, which the people of Makkah would have seen.

Moreover, as people regularly come to Makkah, news would have reached them of the preparation of an army or people coming from outside would have seen it and warned them of it. Despite not seeing the army, not hearing the army, not being informed of the army nor witnessing any indication towards the existence of the army, all those present testified that they believed Rasulullah ﷺ.

Rasulullah ﷺ was trying to elucidate towards the fact that they may not have seen, heard, been informed about nor witnessed anything which indicates towards what he preached. Just as they had believed him with regards to the army they too should believe him in what he preaches.

Observe how much faith the people had in Rasulullah ﷺ. They were willing to blindly believe him regarding the army, despite not having perceived any signs of the army with their senses. This brings to question our faith in the words of Rasulullah ﷺ. Though the people of Makkah denied the apostleship of Rasulullah ﷺ their actions spoke of their belief in his words. On the other hand we testify to the apostleship of Rasulullah ﷺ but our actions depict denial.

Contemplate over the witness the people of Makkah bore in the words of Rasulullah ﷺ when he addressed them from Mount Safa. Though everything indicated towards the contrary the people firmly believed that if Rasulullah ﷺ alleged there was an army on the other side of the mountain then it is undoubtedly true. We bear witness to the truth of Rasulullah ﷺ, so why do our actions not conform to our testimony?

عَنْ أَنَسِ بْنِ مَالِكٍ . رضى الله عنه . عَنِ النَّبِيِّ صلى الله عليه وسلم قَالَ " وَكَّلَ اللَّهُ بِالرَّحِمِ مَلَكًا فَيَقُولُ أَىْ رَبِّ نُطْفَةٌ، أَىْ رَبِّ عَلَقَةٌ، أَىْ رَبِّ مُضْغَةٌ. فَإِذَا أَرَادَ اللَّهُ أَنْ يَقْضِيَ خَلْقَهَا قَالَ أَىْ رَبِّ ذَكَرٌ أَمْ أُنْثَى أَشَقِيٌّ أَمْ سَعِيدٌ فَمَا الرِّزْقُ فَمَا الأَجَلُ فَيُكْتَبُ كَذَلِكَ فِي بَطْنِ أُمِّهِ "

"Anas bin Malik ﷺ narrates from the Messenger ﷺ that he said, "Allah has given charge to an angel in the womb (of the mother). So the angel proclaims, 'O my Lord! It is now a drop of sperm (fertilized ovum), O my Lord! It is now something that clings. O my Lord! It is now a piece of flesh.' When Allah decides to complete its creation, the angel asks, "O my

Lord! (What shall I write), male or female? Whether wretched or blessed? How much will its sustenance be? What will its age be? So all that is written whilst it is still in the womb of its mother."

(Sahih al-Bukhari)

Rasulullah ﷺ has told us that our share of wealth and provisions had already been stipulated before we were born. Where is our faith in these words? Why do we continue to labour behind the portion of this world which has already been predetermined for us? Why do we not make the most of the lifespan which has been fixed for us?

Sa'd bin Mu'adh ؓ was a friend of Umayyah bin Khalaf. Whenever Umayyah used to pass by Madinah he would stay at Sa'd's ؓ house and whenever Sa'd ؓ passed through Makkah he would stay at Umayyah's house. Rasulullah ﷺ and the Sahabah had emigrated from Makkah to Madinah.

After the migration, Sa'd ؓ went for Umrah. He stayed over at Umayyah's house in Makkah. He said to Umayyah, *"Find for me a time of isolation, so that I can circumambulate the Ka'bah."* Sa'd ؓ was a Muslim and he wanted to avoid confrontation with the Pagans, thus he asked for a time when people would be in their homes in order to circumambulate peacefully.

He came out with Umayyah close to midday, when it is hottest and people retire to their homes to shelter themselves from the excessive heat. On the way to the Ka'bah they were met by Abu Jahl, who asked, *"O Abu Safwan, who is this with you?"* (Abu Safwan was the teknonym of Umayyah, a teknonym is a name for an adult derived from that of a child, especially that of the eldest child)

Umayyah replied, *"This is Sa'd."*

Abu Jahl said to Sa'd ؓ, *"Do you not see that you are circumambulating in Makkah peacefully, whereas you have given shelter to those who have left their religion? You think that you can help them and aid them. I take an oath by Allah if you were not with Abu Safwan you would not return to your family safely."*

Raising his voice Sa'd 🕮 replied to him, "*I take an oath by Allah that if you were to prevent me from this I would prevent you from something which is more severe to you than this is; your road pass Madinah.*"

Umayyah said to Sa'd 🕮, "*O Sa'd, don't raise your voice to Abul Hakam, the leader of the people of the valley.*" (Abul Hakam is the real name of Abu Jahl. Abul Hakam means 'the father of wisdom', but due to not accepting Islam he was renamed Abu Jahl which means 'the father of ignorance'.)

Sa'd 🕮 retorted, "*Leave us O Umayyah, I take an oath by Allah that I heard the Messenger of Allah 🕮 saying, 'They (the Sahabah) are going to kill you.'*"

Umayyah flustered, "*In Makkah?*"

To which Sa'd 🕮 replied, "*I don't know.*"

Umayyah was terribly frightened by this news. When he returned home he confided in his wife, "*O Umm Safwan! Did you not see what Sa'd said to me?*"

She asked, "*And what did he say to you?*"

He answered, "*He alleges Muhammad informed them that they (the Sahabah) are going to kill me.*"

She asked, "*In Makkah?*"

He said, "*I do not know.*" Umayyah made a firm resolve saying, "*I take an oath by Allah I will not leave Makkah.*"

When the day of Badr dawned upon them, Abu Jahl was mobilising the people. He told them to prepare their mounts. Umayyah detested the idea of leaving for the battle due to the fear of Rasulullah's 🕮 words, stating the Sahabah were going to kill him. But Abu Jahl came to him and said, "*O Abu Safwan, when the people see that you have remained behind, whereas you are a leader of the people of the valley, they too will remain behind.*"

Abu Jahl continued insisting upon his joining the army until Umayyah resigned to Abu Jahl's persistence. Umayyah said, "*Seeing as you have overwhelmed me, I take an oath by Allah, I will buy the finest camel in*

Makkah." Then Umayyah said, *"O Umm Safwan, prepare me."*

She questioned him, *"O Abu Safwan have you forgotten what your Yathribi brother said to you?"* (His Yathribi brother was Sa'd ﷺ, Madinah was previously known as Yathrib)

He answered, *"No (I have not forgotten), I do not intend to go with them except a short distance."*

When Umayyah left Makkah, journeying towards Badr, he would not alight at any place except that he would keep his camel close at hand. He intended to turn back at every point, but Abu Jahl would keep insisting that he goes a little further. This continued until Allah killed him at Badr.

From this incident, we can glean the conviction that the disbelievers had in the words of Rasulullah ﷺ. When Sa'd ﷺ told Umayyah that Rasulullah ﷺ had stated the Sahabah were going to kill him, he did not react to this by asking, *'What does he know?'* or *'How would he know?'* He immediately believed that he was going to be killed, thus he asked if he was going to be killed in Makkah. He had such faith in Rasulullah's ﷺ words that if he could find out where the Sahabah were going to kill him then he would have avoided going to that place. Furthermore he did not leave it at that, rather he went home and informed his wife. His wife's question was the same. They did not doubt Rasulullah ﷺ at all. To the extent that the truth of what Rasulullah ﷺ had foretold was embedded in them such that he was afraid to leave Makkah.

Reflect over the certainty and confidence Umayyah and his wife had in the words of Rasulullah ﷺ. They attested to this not only in words but in action also. If these people who denied Rasulullah ﷺ had such firm conviction in his words then how much greater should the conviction be of one who affirms, testifies and bears witness that Muhammad ﷺ is the messenger of Allah?

Ibrahim ibn Ad'ham ﷺ was a pious ascetic, who was born in a place called Balkh. He was adopted by the King of Balkh and raised up in his palace. As the king had no apparent heir, he appointed him as his successor and thus he became the king after him. He was inclined towards righteousness and piety and would make the following prayer, *"O Allah! I desire to be connected with you. I long for your closeness."*

One narration states, he was resting in his bedroom when he heard a clamour on the roof above him. When he asked someone to investigate the cause of the disturbance, a man was brought forth. Ibrahim ibn Ad'ham ﷺ asked him, *"How did you get on the roof? What were you doing there?"*

The man replied, *"I have lost my camels."*

Ibrahim ibn Ad'ham ﷺ retorted, *"If you have lost your camels you should look for them in the desert or wilderness, not in a palace! Who can be more ignorant than the one who searches for camels on a palace roof?"*

The man replied, *"The one who searches for Allah sitting on a royal throne."* These words had a profound effect on him. It is has been narrated he left his kingdom and set off to search for Allah immediately.

He left without notifying his people of his departure, so his soldiers, governors and ministers set out in search of him. After a long time they found him sitting by the ocean in a tattered state sewing his quilt. Upon seeing him in this condition they attempted to persuade him to return by mentioning all the comforts and luxuries of the kingdom he had left behind. They pleaded, *"Live as you wish amongst us, but remain our king. We need your shade over us. Why have you left us?"*

Ibrahim ibn Ad'ham ﷺ threw the needle, with which he was sewing his quilt, into the ocean and called out, *"My needle!"* Thousands of fish appeared with golden needles in their mouths, but none had his original needle. He asked for his needle to be brought forth and a small fish surfaced with his needle in its mouth. Ibrahim ibn Ad'ham ﷺ took the needle and said, *"My kingdom now extends over the land and sea, what do I need your insignificant kingdom for?"*

The world is such that the more we continue to chase it the more it will distance itself from us. But if we turn our backs to the world then it will come and lay itself at our feet. Take the example of Ibrahim ibn Ad'ham ﷺ, he left his kingdom to gain closeness to Allah for which Allah made the world subservient to him. What need would one have for a kingdom when they have the owner of the universe?

We have not been created to earn this world. We have been created to recognise Allah. So let us reflect over our purpose in life and what direction we are headed.

قَالَ رَسُولُ اللهِ صَلَّى اللهُ عَلَيْهِ وَسَلَّمَ: لَلَّهُ أَشَدُّ فَرَحًا بِتَوْبَةِ عَبْدِهِ حِينَ يَتُوبُ إِلَيْهِ، مِنْ أَحَدِكُمْ كَانَ عَلَى رَاحِلَتِهِ بِأَرْضٍ فَلَاةٍ، فَانْفَلَتَتْ مِنْهُ وَعَلَيْهَا طَعَامُهُ وَشَرَابُهُ، فَأَيِسَ مِنْهَا، فَأَتَى شَجَرَةً، فَاضْطَجَعَ فِي ظِلِّهَا، قَدْ أَيِسَ مِنْ رَاحِلَتِهِ، فَبَيْنَا هُوَ كَذَلِكَ إِذَا هُوَ بِهَا، قَائِمَةً عِنْدَهُ، فَأَخَذَ بِخِطَامِهَا، ثُمَّ قَالَ مِنْ شِدَّةِ الْفَرَحِ: اللهُمَّ أَنْتَ عَبْدِي وَأَنَا رَبُّكَ، أَخْطَأَ مِنْ شِدَّةِ الْفَرَحِ

The Messenger of Allah ﷺ said, *"Verily Allah is more pleased with the repentance of His slave when he turns to Him than one of you who is on his mount in a waterless desert and loses his camel, on which is his food and water. So he retires to a tree and lies down in its shade having lost all hope of (finding) his camel. Whilst he is in this state (expecting death) he finds that camel standing in front of him. He seizes its reins and out of ecstatic joy he blurts out, 'O Allah you are my slave and I am your Lord.' He makes a mistake out of extreme happiness."*(Due to the endless joy he feels he mistakenly switched it around.)

(Sahih al-Muslim)

عَنْ أَبِي مُوسَى، عَنِ النَّبِيِّ صَلَّى اللهُ عَلَيْهِ وَسَلَّمَ، قَالَ: إِنَّ اللهَ عَزَّ وَجَلَّ يَبْسُطُ يَدَهُ بِاللَّيْلِ لِيَتُوبَ مُسِيءُ النَّهَارِ، وَيَبْسُطُ يَدَهُ بِالنَّهَارِ لِيَتُوبَ مُسِيءُ اللَّيْلِ، حَتَّى تَطْلُعَ الشَّمْسُ مِنْ مَغْرِبِهَا.

Abu Moosa ﷺ narrates from the Messenger ﷺ, that he said, *"Verily Allah ﷺ keeps his arms wide open at night, in order to accept the repentance of the one who sins during the day. And he keeps his arms wide open during the day, in order to accept the repentance of the one who sins during the night, He will continue to do this until the sun rises from its west."*(The sun will rise from the west close to the day of judgement after which repentance will not be accepted).

(Sahih al-Muslim)

These two ahaadith give evidence of Allah's happiness at the repentance of his slave and Allah's eagerness to accept the repentance of His slave.

The man to whom his camel returned feels as though he has been given life after death. The ecstasy he would feel is indescribable.

Take the example of a father whose son ran away from home. For many years he did not hear any news of his son. Every day and night he stands at the entrance of his house. He forsakes all his worldly needs and desires. He no longer finds any pleasure in his food, his drink and in the luxuries of life. He spends every waking moment looking towards the horizon, gazing for a sign of his son. For years he stands there never losing hope. Then one day, whilst standing at his door, he sees his son walking towards his house. Imagine the father's ecstasy; how would he react. He would rush towards him with his arms wide open anticipating the moment he can embrace him. In a hadith Allah says, "When he (i.e. my slave) comes to Me walking, I go to him running." Similarly we are disobedient slaves who have turned away from Allah, but Allah has His arms wide open day and night waiting for the moment we turn to Him in repentance, so that He can readily forgive us. And when that slave walks towards Allah then Allah will rush towards him.

I pray that by reading some of the incidents from the life of Rasulullah ﷺ we are reminded of our true purpose in life and they serve as a means of strengthening our faith. We should further realise from these stories that in Rasulullah ﷺ there is an exemplary example for us. Success in this life and the hereafter lies only in following the way of Rasulullah ﷺ.

اللهم إني أسالك حبك، وحب من يحبك، والعمل الذي يبلغني حبك، اللهم اجعل حبك أحب إليّ من نفسي ومالي وأهلي، ومن الماء البارد

"O Allah, Verily I ask you for your love and the love of those that love you and those actions which allow me to attain your love. O Allah, make your love more beloved to me than myself, my wealth, my family and cold water."

Ameen.

قيل الليل أظلم قبل الضحى   لهذا ولد محمد ﷺ عند الصباح

لما بلغ ظلام الكفر عنان السماء   طلع كالشمس وملأ الدنيا بالضياء

"They say the night is darkest before the dawn.

Thus it was in the morning, when Muhammad ﷺ was born.

When the darkness of disbelief had reached the sky's height,

He came like the sun and filled the world with light."

- Abu Muhammad, Qasim ibn Inayat Ali -

Arabia before

Rasulullah's ﷺ Birth

The people of Makkah had gone astray.

To man-made idols, they would pray.

Around the Ka'bah, many idols they did place.

In their worship, towards them they would face.

They had forgotten the religion which Ibrahim ﷺ taught.

From the useless idols, good fortune they sought.

Instead of Allah, the idols Hubal, Laat and Uzza they praised.

They no longer believed that after they die they would be raised.

They would regularly gamble and drink wine.

Of the religion of Ibrahim ﷺ, there was no sign.

They used to oppress the poor and the weak.

In the world, sin and vice had reached its peak.

Over petty issues the tribes would begin to fight.

Though their ancestors were one, they would not unite.

They would not forget the incidents of the past.

For many years, their civil wars would last.

Some buried their daughters alive out of shame.[1]

Like items and commodities, women became.

Over them there was no leader or king,

Who truth and justice, to them, could bring.

In Arabia, partners to Allah they did ascribe.

In Makkah resided the Quraish tribe.

In this tribe there was the Banu Hashim clan.

In them, the blood of Isma'eel ﷺ ran.

The Banu Hashim, Abdul Muttalib did lead.

The pilgrims to Makkah, he used to feed.

Abdullah was the name of one of the many sons he had.

Abdullah was Allah's beloved Messenger's ﷺ dad.

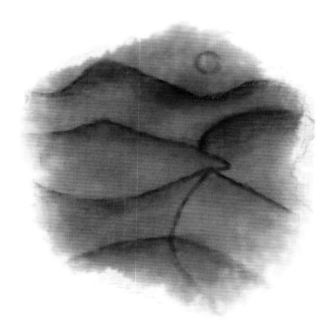

How stars beautify the dark sky so too does good character beautify man who is enshrouded in the darkness of his sins.

The Year of the Elephant

The leader of Yemen was a man called Abrahah.

He was jealous pilgrims flocked to visit the Ka'bah.

He decided to build a beautiful Church of his own.

But towards his house of worship no interest was shown.[2]

The idea of competition with the Ka'bah, the Arabs did hate.

An Arab, from Kinanah, went to his Church to defecate.

This was done in retaliation to his Church, Abrahah came to know.

He was enraged; to destroy the Ka'bah, he decided to go.

To Makkah, with an army of elephants, Abrahah came.

To break down the house of Allah was his aim.

The might of his army, the people of Makkah saw.

To save their lives, to the mountains they did go.

The surrounding areas, Abrahah's army did raid.

By Abdul Muttalib, to Abrahah, a visit was paid.

Abrahah's army had stolen his camels, when they did attack.

Abdul Muttalib went to Abrahah to ask for them back.

Abdul Muttalib was very handsome, Abrahah saw.

Upon seeing him, Abrahah was filled with awe.

With great courtesy, Abdul Muttalib, he did greet.

He offered to sit beside him, having come down from his seat.

To ask what Abdul Muttalib wanted, for an interpreter he called.
Abdul Muttalib wanted his camels returned, Abrahah was told.
When Abdul Muttalib first entered, Abrahah, he did impress,
But due to his demand, Abrahah's esteem for him had become less.

Abrahah was surprised he had come to ask for his camels return,
Towards the Ka'bah, Abdul Muttalib did not show any concern.
Abdul Muttalib explained to Abrahah; *"The camels belong to me,*
While Allah is the Lord of the Ka'bah, and will protect it," said he

Abdul Muttalib got his camels back; to the mountains he did retreat.
Abdul Muttalib knew that the army of Abrahah, they could not defeat.
The next morning, to destroy the Ka'bah, Abrahah did intend.
To protect the Ka'bah, flocks upon flocks of birds, Allah did send

To save his house from being destroyed, Allah willed.
The little birds dropped stones on them; the army they killed.[3]
When they saw this, Abrahah and the rest of the army fled.
Whilst returning Abrahah, caught an infection; he was soon dead.

It is the height of foolishness of the foolish one to question the wisdom of the wise.

From Birth to Marriage

Rasulullah's ﷺ Birth

Abdullah was his father, Amina his mother.

He had neither a sister nor any brother.

Before he was born, his father had passed away.

Rasulullah ﷺ was born in the morning, on a Monday.

In the Year of the Elephant, in Rabi ul-Awwal he was born.[4]

Darkness was to vanish; it was a new era's dawn.

To the desert Bedouins, their children the Arabs sent.

So with Halimah Sa'diyah ﷺ to Banu Sa'd Rasulullah ﷺ went.

Bedouins were more proficient in speech.

Pure Arabic to the children they would teach.

In the desert environment, cleaner was the air,

So Arabs wanted their children to be raised there.

In Banu S'ad

Halimah 🌸 says, "*In the towns for children we went to look,*

With me was my husband, and our baby we took.

It was a year of famine and a year of drought,

Riding on an old donkey, with some women we set out.'

'During the night, we were unable to sleep,

Because out of hunger, our child would weep,

There was no milk with which our baby we could feed.

To the heavens, for rain and relief we would plead."

To the women for suckling, Rasulullah 🌸 was offered,

As he was an orphan, they rejected what was proffered.

As Rasulullah's 🌸 father had passed away before he was born,

They expected no reward; towards him no interest was shown.

A child, every woman from her clan did receive,

Except for Halimah 🌸; empty handed she was going to leave.

She thought, 'Every woman has a child except for me.'

She decided to take the orphan, hoping a blessing he might be.

Along with them, their camel they had brought.

But it would not give them the milk they sought.

With the blessed child, to her camel's saddle she went,

Surprisingly the camel gave milk; they drank to their hearts content.

Her baby, who had been so hungry, was now fed.

He no longer cried; he slept peacefully in his bed.

In the morning, when Halimah ﷺ and her husband awoke,

About Rasulullah ﷺ being a blessed child, they spoke.

The donkey, with which she came to Makkah, was weak and lean,

It lagged behind the others; difficult the journey to Makkah had been.

Now it travelled so fast; people could not believe it was the same,

They asked Halimah ﷺ, "Is that the donkey with which you came?"[5]

When they reached home, more blessings were seen.

Due to drought and famine, their goats were very lean.[6]

When Rasulullah ﷺ arrived, milk the goats began to give.

Until he was weaned, for two years with them he did live.

Halimah ﷺ took him to Makkah; she requested to keep him longer,

There was an illness in Makkah; in the desert he would become stronger.

After much persistence, Amina finally gave into their request.

So back to Banu Sa'd, went the child who was blessed.

One day, Rasulullah ﷺ was outside with his foster brother,

When this brother of his went running back to his mother.

The foster brother was worried and was quite shaken,

He stammered, "My Quraishi brother by two men has been taken."

"There were two men; in white they were dressed,

They laid him down and had cut open his chest."

Rasulullah's ﷺ face was pale when they arrived at the scene.

Jibra'eel ﷺ had come; Rasulullah's ﷺ heart he did clean.

This incident which had occurred, Halimah ؓ it did scare.

Along with her husband, she worried about his welfare.

There was something about him, they now came to know.

So back to his mother, Amina, they decided to go.

Surprised they had returned so soon, Amina did say,

"Why have you come back, when you wanted him to stay?"

To come up with a believable excuse Halimah ؓ did fail.

So to Rasulullah's ﷺ mother, she related the true tale.

"I fear a devil over him," Halimah ؓ finally did say.

Amina replied, "Never! Over him Shaytaan will not have his way.

At his birth, by a light the palaces of Syria, to me, were shown.

He caused me no pain, not even on the day he was born."

His Mother Passes Away

Till the age of six, with his mother he did stay.

To the City of Madinah, they went one day.

Returning from Madinah, his mother passed away.

Now with his grandfather, Abdul Muttalib, he did stay.[7]

Abdul Muttalib preferred Rasulullah ﷺ over the rest.

He preferred him over his sons; he treated him the best.

When Rasulullah ﷺ was eight, his grandfather died.

After this with his uncle, Abu Talib, he did reside.

Rasulullah's ﷺ Youth

Great affection towards Rasulullah ﷺ, Abu Talib did show.

He gave him precedence over his children; he loved him more.

Abu Talib was a merchant; once he went to Sham to trade.[8]

With him was his nephew; the journey to Sham they made.

In Sham, the signs of apostleship in Muhammad ﷺ, a monk saw.

Fearing for Rasulullah ﷺ, he told Abu Talib, *"Further you must not go."*

The Jews would harm him if they recognised him; the monk did fear.

The signs of the Messenger Muhammad ﷺ, in their holy books were clear.

In his youth, his family's cattle he used to herd.

He grew into an honest man; a man of his word.

His honesty and trustworthiness became of fame.

Due to which al-Amin became his nickname.[9]

Of Rasulullah's ﷺ honesty, a wealthy woman named Khadijah ؓ did learn.

She sent him to Sham to trade; where great profit Rasulullah ﷺ did earn.

To Sham, Khadijah ؓ had also told her slave, Maysarah, to go.

Upon their return, from Maysarah, of his qualities she came to know.

Khadijah ؓ was a rich widow; many wanted to marry her.

Her desire to marry Rasulullah ﷺ, to a relative she did confer.[10]

Rasulullah ﷺ was twenty-five years old, and forty was she.

To marry Khadijah ؓ, the blessed Messenger ﷺ did agree.

Though death is inevitable, youth seems eternal.

From Marriage to

Apostleship

The Reconstruction of the Ka'bah

The walls of the Ka'bah had become weak.

To reconstruct the Ka'bah, the Quraish did seek.

But to bring down the walls, nobody dared.

Of a punishment, descending upon them, people were scared.

A portion of the Ka'bah was given to each clan.

Eventually, to take the first step, stood up one man.

From the portion of his clan, he pulled down a part.

When nothing happened to him, the work did start.[11]

Stones for building the Ka'bah, on his shoulders, Rasulullah ﷺ collected.

His uncle Abbas ؓ suggested *"Put your loincloth on your neck, so it is protected."*

As he did this, Rasulullah ﷺ fell to the ground and his eyes turned to the sky.

Upon awakening he covered his loins; he was protected by Allah Most-High.[12]

The Black Stone

The building of the Ka'bah was almost complete,

To place the sacred black stone, the clans began to compete.

Wanting the honour of placing it, oaths were sworn,

They would not be robbed of placing the black stone.[13]

Competition was fierce; civil war nearly began.

To them, an idea was put forward by one man.[14]

'The next person to come through the Suffah gate,

For this heated dispute he will arbitrate.'

Standing together, for the next person they did wait.

Rasulullah ﷺ was the first one to pass through the gate.

Everyone was happy, for it was al-Amin who came through.

They put forward the problem; they asked, 'what should we do?'

For his trustworthiness, Rasulullah ﷺ was renown,

On a blanket he put the sacred black stone down.

To lift the edge of the sheet, the elders of each clan he bade.

Upon reaching the Ka'bah, in its place the stone Rasulullah ﷺ laid.[15]

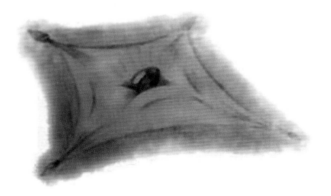

Rasulullah's ﷺ Family

To Rasulullah ﷺ, six children Khadijah ﷺ bore.

Two of them sons, and daughters he had four.[16]

His two sons passed away in infancy, Abdullah and Qasim.

Khadijah ﷺ had given him a slave, Zaid ﷺ, so he adopted him.[17]

As years passed, the qualities of Rasulullah ﷺ people did adore.

Whereas the religion of his people, Rasulullah ﷺ did abhor.

From the evil and vices of the people, he wanted to get away.

So for many days, in contemplation in the cave of Hira he would stay.[18]

Intelligence is overrated, wisdom is not.

The First Revelation

(Ramadhan – 1ˢᵗ Year of Prophethood)

Whatever Rasulullah ﷺ dreamt, it would turn out to be real.[19]

He secluded himself in a cave; with him he would take his meal.

He would contemplate upon Allah and there he would stay.

He would reflect for many nights together, and for many a day.

He received revelation whilst in this state he was engaged.

It was on a Monday and Rasulullah ﷺ had forty years aged.

The angel Jibra'eel ﷺ suddenly appeared; *"Read!"* he said.

To which the Messenger ﷺ replied, *"I am unread"*.

The angel then squeezed him so hard that he felt pain.

Letting him go, he ordered, *"Read;"* the same thing happened again.

The angel embraced him a third time until he could bear no more.

This time the angel Jibra'eel ﷺ read the following, when he let go:

"Read in the name of your Lord who created,

Created man from a blood clot.

Read and your Lord is most bountiful, who taught by the pen,

Taught man that which he knew not."[20]

Rasulullah ﷺ rushed home to Khadijah ؓ, his devoted wife.

She covered him with a blanket; he confided, *"I fear for my life."*

She consoled him, *"Allah will not disgrace you do not despair,*

You join ties of relationship, for the burdened, needy and guest you care."

She took him to her cousin, Waraqah bin Nawfal ⁕, blind and old.[21]

In detail, of Rasulullah's ⁕ experience at Hira he was told.

He replied, *"That was the angel sent to Moosa, now he had prophethood.*

If I were alive when your people exile you from Makkah, help you I would."[22]

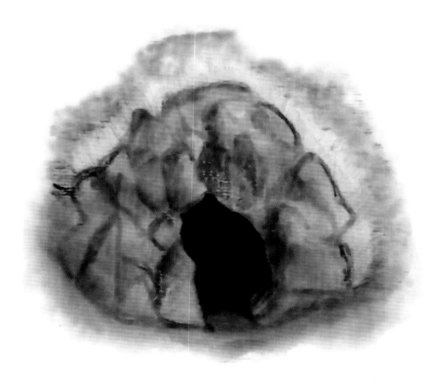

Ilm (knowledge) is an everlasting candle which does not benefit unless lit with the flame of aml (acting upon it).

Preaching Begins

Propagation in Secret

After the incident in Hira, in revelation there was a pause.

Not receiving further revelation, to Rasulullah ﷺ anxiety this did cause.

Then one day whilst he was walking, a voice from the sky, he heard.

The angel Jibra'eel ﷺ had returned to reveal to him Allah's word.

Looking to the sky, he saw the angel Jibra'eel ﷺ was there,

Between the earth and the sky, he was seated on a chair.

Upon seeing him again, afraid Rasulullah ﷺ felt,

On the ground, the Messenger of Allah ﷺ knelt.

Upon reaching home, *"Cover me,"* to his wife he did say.

Revelation started to come more frequently after this day.

He was covered in a blanket; afraid Rasulullah ﷺ did feel.

Whilst in this state the first verses of Surah Muddath'thir Allah did reveal.[23]

Allah commanded Rasulullah ﷺ to *'arise and warn.'*

The true religion to the people was to be shown.

To bring people on the right path was now his aim.

The oneness of Allah, to the world he must proclaim.

Initially, Rasulullah ﷺ only told a select few.

Those he knew who would believe him to be true.

From amongst them Khadijah ﷺ, Abu Bakr ﷺ, Zaid ﷺ and Ali ﷺ,

All accepted Rasulullah's ﷺ call to Islam readily.

About the new religion, people they told,

More and more people entered Islam's fold.

At first in secret the propagation was done.

The hearts of a few people, Rasulullah ﷺ had won.

Open Propagation

News of the new religion, to the Makkan leaders did leak.

They felt that Rasulullah ﷺ and his followers were weak.

But as news of Islam in the people began to spread,

Over their false religion, the leaders began to dread.

'Warn your tribe of near kindred,' Rasulullah ﷺ was told.

Climbing on top of mount Safa, various tribes Rasulullah ﷺ called.

Upon hearing his call, to Mount Safa, they made their way.

The tribes gathered to hear what Rasulullah ﷺ had to say.

"If I say there are some horsemen in the valley planning to raid you,"

Rasulullah ﷺ asked, "Would you take what I say to be true?"

They replied, "Yes, from you we have never experienced a lie."

To establish to the people he was truthful, Rasulullah ﷺ did try.[24]

Rasulullah ﷺ said, "I am a warner to you of a severe torment."

Abu Lahab retorted, "May you perish, is this why for us you sent!"

The Makkans burst into outrage and refused to accept his appeal.

On this occasion 'Perish the two hands of Abu Lahab' Allah did reveal.

The religion of their forefathers, the Makkans did not want to leave.

In the truth of Rasulullah's ﷺ words, they refused to believe.

To them, the idea of life after death had become absurd.

The Makkans alleged the Qur'an was a madman's word.

Fulfilling your needs will satiate you, whilst fulfilling your desires will make you hungrier.

Persecution

Abu Talib's Support

Within Makkah, the religion of Islam started to spread.

"We cannot tolerate this," the leaders of Makkah said.

To protect Rasulullah ﷺ, his uncle, Abu Talib did guarantee.

So for a solution to their problem, Abu Talib they went to see.

They told him, *"Your nephew, from preaching, you must dissuade."*

To relinquish his protection, Abu Talib they were unable to persuade.

To try and change Abu Talib's mind, to him, they went again.

But their efforts to win Rasulullah's ﷺ uncle over were in vain.

Finally they went to him; and in front of him they took an oath,

That if he does not stop his nephew, they would fight them both.

Abu Talib had not converted, but his nephew he did not want to betray.

"Do not cause me to carry a burden I cannot bear," to his nephew he did say.

"If they put the sun in my right hand and the moon in my left," Rasulullah ﷺ said,

"I would not leave this cause, until Allah vindicated it or I was dead."

Upon hearing the determination in what Rasulullah ﷺ did say,

Abu Talib replied, *"Go and say what you will, you I will never betray."*

The Persecution of Early Converts

Compared to the polytheists, in numbers the Muslims were less.

So persecution began because, the oneness of Allah, they did confess.

Bilal was made to lie on the burning sand with a boulder on his chest.

Despite the hardship, *"Allah is one, Allah is one,"* he professed.

On hot burning coals, Khabbab ✿ was made to lie.

Due to the fat melting off his back, the coals would die.[25]

A rope would be tied around a believers feet.

He would then be dragged around on a hot rocky street.

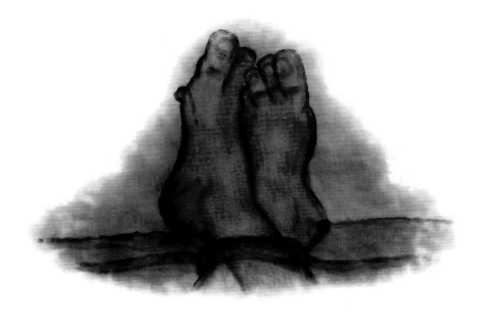

Yasir ✿, Summayyah ✿ and their son Ammar ✿ were a family.

By the disbelievers they would be tortured mercilessly.

But they were not shaken; in their faith they were sincere.

Then one day Summayyah ✿ was martyred; killed with a spear.[26]

They threw the entrails of a camel upon Rasulullah's ﷺ back, whilst he did pray.

Umm Jamil, the wife of Abu Lahab, would regularly throw rubbish in his way.

Many of the companions of Rasulullah ﷺ were tortured; whilst some were killed.

But in them truth, steadfastness and the oneness of Allah was instilled.

Many of the early Muslims were the slaves, the weak and the poor.

Of receiving reward for their patience, Rasulullah ﷺ would assure.

Whenever a slave being tortured by their master, Abu Bakr ﷺ would see,

He would buy the slave from them and would then set them free.[27]

The Bribe

Despite the persecution, to renounce their religion the Muslims refused.

For a plan to stop Rasulullah ﷺ from his preaching, the disbelievers mused.

To come up with a solution, gathered the leaders of each tribe.

They decided to try and sway Rasulullah ﷺ with a bribe.

Utbah said to Rasulullah ﷺ, "If wealth you desire, wealth we will bring,

If leadership is what you desire, we will make you our king,

If you are afflicted with an illness we will pay for its cure.

All we ask from you is that from preaching this religion you abjure."

After Rasulullah ﷺ had listened to him, to Utbah the Qur'an he did recite.

Through which Utbah realised he did not desire, wealth, power or might.

Utbah returned to his people and told them to let Rasulullah ﷺ be.

But with the calculated opinion of Utbah, the leaders did not agree.

The most inconsiderate one is he who put others in a position he himself would not like to be in.

The Migration to Abyssinia

The Two Delegates

The persecution, the Muslims were no longer able to bear.

Some migrated to Abyssinia because a just king ruled there.

The Makkans were furious; these Muslims they could not attack.

So they sent two ambassadors to Abyssinia, to bring them back.

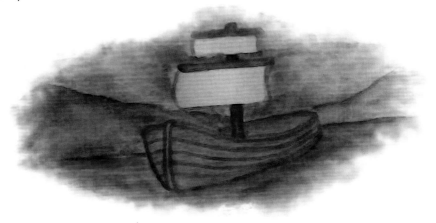

With gifts for King Negus ✾ and his clergy, the two went.

To sway them to their side, the gifts they did present.

They asked the king for the Muslim refugees to be expelled,

And handed over to them, so their dispute can be quelled.

They claimed that the religion of their forefathers, they did leave.

In a religion, different from theirs and the king's they did believe.[28]

The king was just, and from believing them he did refrain.

He called for the Muslims, to give them a chance to explain.

Ja'far's Reply

King Negus ﷺ summoned the Muslims to his court.
He asked them with regards to what their religion taught.
The Muslims had decided that the whole truth they would tell.
Upon Ja'far ﷺ, the son of Abu Talib, the responsibility fell.

"O King, we were drowning in ignorance," Ja'far ﷺ said,
"We worshipped idols, we were unchaste, and we ate dead.[29]
We spoke bad and did not care for the rights of humanity,
Nor did we uphold the rights of the neighbour or show hospitality."

Ja'far ﷺ said, *"We had no law, except we were ruled by the strong."*
He explained how they were indulged in vice and wrong.
"Then Allah raised amongst us a man of whose honesty we did know.
The oneness of Allah and the right path, to us, he did show."

"He forbade the worship of idol, and told us the truth we must speak.
We should fulfil our promises, and have mercy on the weak.
He told us to fulfil the rights of neighbours and of kith and kin,
He ordered us to stay away from evil, vice and sin."

"To offer prayer, give alms and observe fast, he did command.
Due to the persecution from our people, we came to your land."
The Christian king was impressed with Ja'far's ﷺ eloquent speech.
He asked him to recite the words from which Rasulullah ﷺ did teach.

Ja'far ﷺ recited some verses from Surah Maryam; the King began to cry.[30]
He realised these words were from the Lord of Isa ﷺ, Allah, most-High.[31]
He said to the two men, *"I'm afraid I cannot give you back these refugees,*
They are free to live and worship in my country, as they well please."

A Second Attempt

The next day the two men told the king 'about Isa ﷺ, the Muslims lied.'[32]

So the king asked the Muslims regarding Isa ﷺ; again Ja'far ؓ replied.

He said, *"He is the servant and messenger of Allah, we have been taught."*

Pleased with their answer, the king returned the gifts the delegates had brought.[33]

The Second Migration

Some years later, of the persecution stopping, the migrants did learn.[34]

Overjoyed, to Makkah, they decided to return.

When they reached Makkah, they found the news was not true.

In the first emigration to Abyssinia, those who went were few.

They found the Quraish's persecution was stronger than before.

So the Muslims decided to migrate to Abyssinia once more.

Previously, in number, the men were eleven and the women were four.

This time over eighty Muslim men, women and children did go.

Don't destroy your shack because of your neighbour's castle.

Hamzah ﷺ Accepts Islam

(Zhu al-Hijjah – 6th Year of Prophethood)

Rasulullah's ﷺ passage to Mount Safa, Abu Jahl once blocked.

Then he started to harass Rasulullah ﷺ and Islam he mocked.[35]

Of the incident, Rasulullah's ﷺ uncle, Hamzah ﷺ, came to know.

He went to Abu Jahl and hit him on the head with his hunting bow.

"O Hamzah, it seems that you have given up your religion," said he.

Hamzah ﷺ responded, *"I declare he is Allah's messenger, try and stop me!"*[36]

To leave Hamzah ﷺ alone, those who came to help Abu Jahl were told.

Persecution of the Muslims lessened when Hamzah ﷺ entered Islam's fold.

Fear that which is to come, due to that which has gone.

Umar ؓ Accepts Islam

(Zhu al-Hijjah – 6th Year of Prophethood)

Initially, Umar ؓ hated Islam and what Rasulullah ﷺ taught.

One day, to kill the Messenger of Allah ﷺ he sought.

The whereabouts of Rasulullah ﷺ, he came to know.

To him, with his sword in his hand, Umar ؓ did go.

He met Sa'd ibn Abi Waqqas ؓ, a Muslim, on the way.[37]

"I am going to this man, the apostate," Umar ؓ did say.

Sa'd ؓ replied, *"First, towards your family, attention you should pay.*

Do you think Banu Abd Munaf will let you live if Muhammad you slay?"[38]

He learnt, to Islam, his sister and her husband had converted.

Furious, towards his sister's house, his route he diverted.

Umar ؓ approached the house; in it there was a third.

Reciting the Qur'an to his sister and her husband, a man he heard.

They too heard him coming; the man and the Qur'an they did hide.

Without knocking on the door, Umar ؓ burst inside.

There was his sister, Fatimah ؓ, and Sa'eed ؓ, his brother in law.

To Sa'eed ؓ, in a fit of rage, he delivered a strong blow.

When Fatimah ؓ rose to protect her husband, Umar ؓ gave her a blow.

He hit her on the head and caused her blood to flow.

When they saw the blood flowing from her head,

"We have become Muslim, do what you will," the pair said.

Umar ﷺ was moved, when the courage of Fatimah ﷺ and Sa'eed ﷺ, he saw.

He was further ashamed that he had caused blood to flow.

The manuscript from which they had been reading, he asked to see.

His sister Fatimah ﷺ handed it over to him, reluctantly.

Umar ﷺ was touched by the content of what he did read.

A changed man, towards Rasulullah ﷺ, he did proceed.

In front of Rasulullah ﷺ, his conversion to Islam he declared.

To persecute the Muslims in front of Umar ﷺ, nobody dared.

Though one may turn a blind eye, it does not mean he is blind.

The Boycott

(7th Year of Prophethood)

In the Valley

The conversions to Islam, the disbelievers were unable to stem.

They gathered to discuss what should be done to them.

Gathering in Wadi al-Muhassab, they all signed a pact,

'None should marry into Banu Hashim or with them have any contact.'

Only when Banu Hashim hand Rasulullah ﷺ over, the pact they would end.

A signed copy of the agreement, in the Ka'bah, they did suspend.

To a valley to the east of Makkah, Abu Talib and his nephew did withdraw.

Along with him, the Banu Hashim, Banu Muttalib and the Muslims did go.

The pagans of Makkah had stopped their food supply.

Out of hunger, from the valley, one could hear the children cry.

The leaves of trees and animal skins, the Muslims would eat.

Once to his aunt, Khadijah ﵂, Hakeem tried to smuggle some wheat.

Abu Jahl tried to stop him, when Hakeem was seen.

Hakeem managed to give it, when al-Bukhtari did intervene.

The hardships and difficulties increased day by day.

In the valley for three years, the Muslims did stay.

Abu Talib would tell Rasulullah ﷺ to sleep in his place at night.

Then when everyone was asleep, he would move him out of sight.

The assassination of his beloved nephew, he did fear.

Abu Talib had not accepted Islam, yet to him, his nephew was so dear.

The Boycott Ends

To the boycott, some of the restless Makkans did not agree.

From the clauses of the pact, they wanted the Muslims to be free.

One by one, to get rid of the pact, to Abu Jahl they did go.

But Abu Jahl dismissed them saying, 'you all planned this before.'[39]

Revelation that the pact had been eaten, Rasulullah ﷺ had been sent.

To Abu Jahl and the pagan leaders, Abu Talib went.

He informed them of the reason for which he came,

'Ants have eaten the pact, except the part with Allah's name.'[40]

Abu Talib stipulated, "You must stop the boycott, if my nephew is true,

And if he is not then I will hand him over to you."

To the proposition of Abu Talib, the pagan leaders did gladly agree.

They stopped the boycott, when on the pact only Allah's name they did see.[41]

Unity ties U N I together.

The Year of Grief

The Two Supports

Abu Talib was on his death bed, having fallen ill.

Rasulullah ﷺ rushed to him, as time he had still.

He knelt beside his uncle; his uncle he did address,

"O Uncle, in the oneness of Allah, profess."

Abu Jahl and Abdullah bin Umayyah were also at his side.

Whenever Rasulullah ﷺ told him to believe, they both replied,

"The religion of Abdul Muttalib, are you going to leave?"

Fearing the taunt of his people, Abu Talib refused to believe.

To Abu Talib having believed, Rasulullah ﷺ wanted to testify.

But on the religion of his father, Abu Talib did die.

When his uncle passed away, Rasulullah ﷺ was struck with grief.

Even though he knew Rasulullah ﷺ was true, he stuck to his old belief.

This same year, his beloved wife, Khadijah ﷺ, also passed away.

The two supports of Rasulullah ﷺ, under the ground they lay.

When people denied him, Khadijah ﷺ had been the one who believed.

In her person and wealth, much comfort Rasulullah ﷺ had received.

Now that the uncle of Rasulullah ﷺ was no longer there,

The oppression of the Muslims, the pagans did openly declare.

The disbelievers no longer cared, if Rasulullah ﷺ, they hurt.

On one occasion, at Rasulullah ﷺ, one of them threw dirt.

In Search of a Sanctuary

They were unable to bear the hardships, from the Makkans, anymore,.

To spread the word of Islam, to the people of Ta'if, Rasulullah ﷺ did go.

He offered Islam to each leader they rudely turned him down.

The people threw stones at him; they chased him out of their town.

Grief stricken, Rasulullah ﷺ was forced to flee from the town.

Due to the injuries, he became unconscious and fell down.[42]

There was a cloud giving him shade, when he awoke.

Rasulullah ﷺ looked at it; from it the angel Jibra'eel ﷺ spoke.

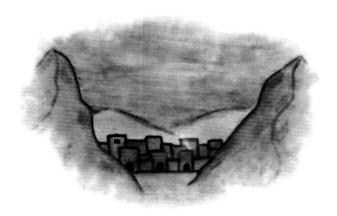

He said, *"Allah has heard what your people have said, and how they have treated you.*

He has sent the angel of the mountains to you; whatever you want with these people, you can do."

Upon Rasulullah ﷺ, by the Angel of the Mountains, salutations were conferred.

Then he said, *"O Muhammad, verily what your nation has said to you Allah has heard."*

"I am the angel of the mountains; Allah has sent me to you,

You can order me with a command; what do you want me to do?"

The angel offered to crush them with two mountains; they would all be dead.

"Rather I hope Allah takes from their progeny, one who worships Allah," Rasulullah ﷺ said.[43]

Rasulullah Remarries

In Shawwal, Rasulullah married a lady called Sawdah.

She was the daughter of a man named Zam'ah.

With her previous husband, to Abyssinia, she did migrate.

When her husband died, she was so fortunate to have Rasulullah in her fate.

Patience makes the life sweeter, for moments plucked before their time will taste bitter.

The Night Journey – al-Isra

In the house of Umm Hani bint Abi Talib🌸, Rasulullah ﷺ did rest,[44]

When suddenly, in front of him, appeared a celestial guest.

It was Jibra'eel ﷺ; the angel who brought revelation from the sky.

Waiting near the Ka'bah was an animal, al-Buraq, which could fly.

When Jibra'eel ﷺ appeared, Rasulullah ﷺ did awaken.

To the Buraq, an animal from paradise, Rasulullah ﷺ was taken.

In size, the Buraq is a steed between a mule and a donkey.

One of it steps is the distance of how far it can see. [45]

Towards Masjid ul-Aqsa, Rasulullah ﷺ was flown.

On the way, many sights to Rasulullah ﷺ were shown.

Rasulullah ﷺ dismounted from the Buraq, which he did ride.

Where the messengers used to tie their mounts, the Buraq he tied.

Into Masjid ul-Aqsa, the Messenger of Allah ﷺ did go.

Allah had assembled all the messengers from before.

After the azhaan and iqaamat were said, [46]

All the messengers in prayer, Rasulullah ﷺ led.[47]

The distinguished importance of one does not diminish the virtue of another.

The Ascension - al-Mi'raaj

With Jibra'eel ﷺ, into the heavens, Rasulullah ﷺ did fly.

Rasulullah ﷺ was going to visit his Lord, most-High.

To open the door, the guardian of the first heaven was told.

The guardian asked who it was and whether they had been called.

"It is Jibra'eel, and Muhammad is with me," Jibra'eel ﷺ replied.

They informed them that they had been called; they were permitted inside.[48]

They reached the first heaven; Adam ﷺ, he did meet.

Adam ﷺ welcomed him and prayed for his well-being, when they did greet.

By the guardians, at each heaven, the questioning occurred.

On each occasion, the same answer they procured.[49]

They reached the second heaven; Yahya ﷺ and Isa ﷺ, he did meet.

They welcomed him and prayed for his well-being, when they did greet.

On the third heaven, the Messenger Yusuf ﷺ he did meet.

He welcomed him and prayed for his well-being, when they did greet.

When he reached the fourth heaven, Idrees ﷺ he did meet.

He welcomed him and prayed for his well-being, when they did greet.

When he reached the fifth heaven, Haroon ﷺ he did meet.

He welcomed him and prayed for his well-being, when they did greet.

When he reached the sixth heaven, Moosa ﷺ he did meet.

He welcomed him and prayed for his well-being, when they did greet.

On the seventh heaven, Ibrahim  was seen.

Against the Bayt ul-Ma'mur, he did lean.[50]

His forefather, Ibrahim ﷺ, Rasulullah ﷺ went to greet.

He said, *"Congratulations, my exalted son,"* when they did meet.

To the Lote Tree of the furthest limit, they came.

Sidrat ul-Muntaha is this point's name.[51]

Jibra'eel ﷺ told Rasulullah ﷺ that he could not carry on anymore.

Beyond this point, to Allah, only Rasulullah ﷺ could go.

On this journey, Rasulullah ﷺ saw heaven and hell,

And of other great sights, narrations do tell.

With Allah, the Almighty, Rasulullah ﷺ spoke.

The lover and beloved surely did talk.

The Gift

Allah granted Rasulullah ﷺ fifty prayers for every night and day.

On his way down, *"What did Allah give you?"* Moosa ﷺ did say.

Fifty prayers had been granted to the Ummah, Moosa ﷺ was told.

The trials and tribulation of Banu Isra' eel, Moosa ﷺ then recalled.

Moosa ﷺ said, *"Your Ummah will not bear this burden, to Allah you must go.*

Request Allah to reduce them, I have been tested with my people before."

They were reduced by five, but Moosa ﷺ told him to reduce them more.

Like this they kept reducing by five; back and forth, Rasulullah ﷺ did go.[52]

When Moosa ﷺ was told there were five prayers left, he was still unsatisfied.

But Rasulullah ﷺ was ashamed to return, *"I submit to divine will,"* he replied.

The burden of his slaves, Allah, the most-Merciful, had made light.

Rasulullah ﷺ returned from this long journey, that very same night.

The Reaction of the Pagans

To the people of Makkah, the Night Journey, Rasulullah ﷺ did confer.

Amongst the blinded disbelievers, the incident created a stir.

The people of Makkah laughed, when to them the Isra and Mi'raaj were related.

However to believe in Rasulullah's ﷺ journey, Abu Bakr ؓ never hesitated.[53]

The faith of Abu Bakr, the people of Makkah tried to sway.

They jeered, "Look at what your companion does say."

They informed him of Rasulullah's ﷺ journey to al-Aqsa, in one night.

Abu Bakr told them, if that is what he asserts, he believed him to be right.

The journey was an impossible one, the pagans thought.

From Rasulullah ﷺ, the description of Jerusalem they sought.

Before this, to Jerusalem, Rasulullah ﷺ had never been.

He furnished an accurate description of what he has seen.

There was no doubt in the matter; to Jerusalem he had been.

He also informed them of the Makkan caravans that he seen.

To all of their questions, the right answers, the pagans did find.

But of the truth in Rasulullah's ﷺ words they had become blind.

The value of all humans is equal in death. Why then is the value of all human life not considered equal?

The Pledge

Rasulullah ﷺ would preach to the pilgrims, when for hajj they would come.

The religion of Islam was rejected by many, and accepted by some.

In the eleventh year of apostleship, six people of Madinah came into Islam's fold.

When they returned to Madinah, towards Allah their people they called.

The following year, from Madinah, twelve men came.

The oneness of Allah, each of them did proclaim.

Near Aqabah, with them, Rasulullah ﷺ made a pact,

That upon the teachings of Islam, they will act.

Mus'ab bin Umair ؓ was sent to Madinah to preach.[54]

The principals and beliefs of Islam, he did teach.

In Madinah, Mus'ab's ؓ preaching was a great success.

The oneness of Allah, many people did profess.

The people of Madinah, Mus'ab ؓ had managed to assuage.

The next year, over seventy set out for pilgrimage.

In a place called Aqabah, they met with Rasulullah ﷺ, at night.

They met under the cover of darkness; wanting to stay out of sight.[55]

His uncle, Abbas ؓ, accompanied him; to the people he did say,

"From the protection of his kindred, do not take Muhammad away.

Unless you are fully prepared to protect him, and his life you must defend.

If not, then leave now, my nephew I will not send."

They promised that Rasulullah ﷺ they would defend.

If he sought their help, they would fight to the end.

They wanted Rasulullah ﷺ to come to Madinah to reside.

Upon the principles of the pledge, they promised to abide.

One man's kindness to another man is what makes us mankind.

The Hijrah – Migration to Madinah

(Safar – 1st Year after Hijrah)

The Migration of Abu Salamah ﷺ and his Family

By migrating to Madinah, their homes the Muslims would lose.

Over worldly possessions, the pleasure of Allah they did choose.

In Makkah, the number of Muslims had greatly dropped.[56]

So the pagans thought of ways in which they could be stopped

Abu Salamah ﷺ, his wife and child were going to migrate.

His wife and child, from him, the pagans did separate.

He had no choice but to leave his wife and son behind.

He set off towards Madinah; a new home he had to find.

For a year his wife, Umm Salamah ﷺ, did cry and grieve,[57]

Finally her family gave her permission to leave.

With her son, she had to travel the dangerous desert alone.

Uthman bin Talhah took them, when he saw them on their own.[58]

The Pagan's Plot

In Makkah, the number of Muslims became less.

Fearing for their power, the pagans were in distress.

In Dar un-Nadwah, the pagan leaders did convene,

To discuss if a solution to their problem could be seen.

Opinions were given to expel Rasulullah ﷺ, or put him in jail.

Each of the suggestions had a flaw, which would make it fail.

Abu Jahl suggested that Rasulullah ﷺ should be assassinated.

With this evil idea of his, the leaders were fascinated.

To the 'Firown of this Ummah's' plan, the leaders agreed.[59]

A youth from each tribe was told to carry out the deed.

When Rasulullah's ﷺ family seek revenge, upon finding him dead,

Unable to exact the killer, blood-money amongst them would be spread.[60]

The Migration of Rasulullah ﷺ

To migrate, Rasulullah ﷺ was waiting for permission from his Lord.

Jibra'eel ﷺ informed him that the Quraish wanted him under the sword.

Rasulullah ﷺ went to Abu Bakr's ﷺ house; he told him to prepare.

Rasulullah ﷺ learnt that Abu Bakr ﷺ had kept a camel for him, there.

At night they surrounded his house; in ambush they lay.

They were waiting for Rasulullah ﷺ to come out to pray.

Rasulullah's ﷺ cousin, Ali ﷺ, was also inside.

Under the covers of his bed, Rasulullah ﷺ told him to hide.

Though in the disbelievers, the hatred for Rasulullah ﷺ ran deep,

Still aware of his honesty, their possessions they would give him to keep.

Now these same people were waiting outside; ready to attack,

But Rasulullah ﷺ told Ali ؓ, 'Make sure to give them their possessions back.'[61]

Surrounding the house, Ali ؓ knew that there were many men armed.

He put his trust in Allah and His Rasul ﷺ; he knew he would not be harmed.

Reciting the holy Qur'an, Rasulullah ﷺ opened the door.

Into the eyes of the disbelievers, dust he did blow.

He walked past them; Rasulullah ﷺ they never saw.

Directly to Abu Bakr's ؓ house, Rasulullah ﷺ did go.

The youth maintained their siege, not knowing he had gotten away.

When they entered his house, they found Ali ؓ; fast asleep he lay.[62]

With anger and fury, the pagan leaders roared.

For the capture of Rasulullah ﷺ, they offered a huge reward.

Abu Bakr ؓ was waiting, as per the instruction Rasulullah ﷺ gave.

They headed south towards Mount Thawr, to hide in a cave.

Madinah was north of Makkah; this was a clever ruse.

When trying to track Rasulullah ﷺ, the pagans it would confuse.[63]

Abu Bakr ؓ entered the cave first and gave it a clean.

He covered up the holes of the cave, to avoid being seen.

Rasulullah ﷺ entered; resting his head on Abu Bakr's ؓ lap he fell asleep.

A poisonous insect stung Abu Bakr's ؓ foot, due to which he began to weep.

Abu Bakr ؓ did not move, but a tear fell on Rasulullah's ﷺ blessed face.

He woke up and put his saliva on the bite; of the poison there was no trace.[64]

Abdullah ibn Abi Bakr ﷺ would go to visit them at night.[65]

He would inform them of the situation; keeping out of sight.

Early in the morning, to Makkah he would return.

Abdullah's ﷺ activities, the disbelievers did not discern.

To Abu Bakr's ﷺ flock, Amir bin Fuhairah ﷺ did tend.

In the evening, to them, goat's milk he would send.

Meanwhile, the pagans had sent riders to give chase.

Of Rasulullah's ﷺ whereabouts, people were looking for a trace.

To the cave on Mount Thawr, a group of disbelievers came near.

Abu Bakr ﷺ was worried; for the life of Rasulullah ﷺ he did fear.

He whispered, *"What if they look through a hole, and we are spied?"*

"What do think of the two with whom Allah is the third?" Rasulullah ﷺ replied.[66]

Abdullah bin Uraiqit had been hired to be their guide.

On the third day, he arrived with their camels, to where they did hide.

Abu Bakr ﷺ offered Rasulullah ﷺ the faster camel to ride.

"Only if you allow me to pay for it," Rasulullah ﷺ replied.[67]

Of Rasulullah's ﷺ whereabouts, Suraqah came to know.[68]

To redeem the reward, to capture them he did go.

In the direction of Rasulullah ﷺ, on a swift horse he was bound.

Suddenly his horse stumbled, and he fell to the ground.

To decide whether to do something, pagans used to draw out a lot.

Suraqah drew one, to decide whether to give chase or not.

Not to go any further, the lot he drew showed.

But Suraqah longed for the 'hundred camel reward'.[69]

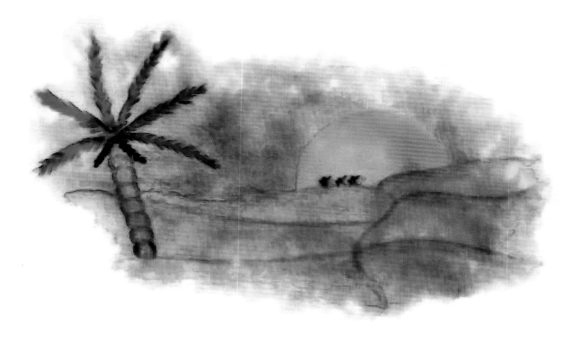

Again his horse stumbled, and he fell to the ground.

Again when drawing lots, the same result he found.

Repeatedly his horse would stumble, and he would fall.

He realised he would not catch them; for forgiveness he did call.[70]

Suraqah understood that Rasulullah ﷺ was going to have the upper-hand.

He related, to him, everything the people of Quraish had planned.

He offered Rasulullah ﷺ provisions, which Rasulullah ﷺ politely declined,

Rasulullah ﷺ asked him to make their whereabouts difficult to find.[71]

The Loyal Companion

One day, they were looking for shade from the unbearable heat.

Abu Bakr ﷺ found some shade by a rock; beside it he laid a sheet.

He went in search for food, whilst Rasulullah ﷺ rested in the shade.

Towards his exhaustion and hunger, no attention Abu Bakr ﷺ paid.

He met a shepherd boy, whilst for food he did look.

With his permission, some milk from the goats he took.

Abu Bakr ﷺ cooled the milk with some water first.

Then he waited for Rasulullah ﷺ to wake and quench his thirst.

Whenever anyone asked Abu Bakr ﷺ regarding the man by his side,

He would reply to each of them, *"He is my guide."*

People would think that he was a guide, who showed him the road,

But Abu Bakr ﷺ meant that he was the guide to his final abode.

On the way to Madinah, they came across a tent.

They went towards it, in search of refreshment.

Outside the tent, looking out for travellers, a lady was sat.

Her name was Umm Ma'bad ﷺ; she was sitting on her mat.

When Rasulullah ﷺ asked for milk, she said her only goat was dry,

The rest of the goats had gone to graze; to milk it he could try.

When Rasulullah ﷺ touched the udders, milk began to flow.

They all drank from it; for the lady, in a container, he filled some more.

Abu Ma'bad ﷺ returned after his goats had grazed.

When he saw milk in the house, he was amazed.

No milk was given by the goats, with which he did go.

From his wife, the incident with Rasulullah ﷺ, he came to know.[72]

The people of Madinah learnt that Rasulullah ﷺ had left Makkah to migrate.

Each day they would come to the outskirts; for his arrival they would wait.

They would wait in anticipation, until the heat they could no longer bear.

After waiting for a long time, of his arrival that day, they would despair.

To do some work, a Jew had climbed a great height.

From there he saw three men, who were clad in white.

He realised this was the man, whose arrival, the Arabs anticipated.

He shouted, *"O Arabs, here comes the man for which you waited."*

Taking their weapons, they rushed to Rasulullah's ﷺ side.

To the pledge they had taken, they showed they would abide.

Abu Bakr ؓ was standing, whilst Rasulullah ﷺ quietly took a seat.

They thought he was the Messenger; Abu Bakr ؓ, they began to greet.

After a while, by the rays of the sun, Rasulullah ﷺ was hit.

To shade him, Abu Bakr ؓ stood over him with his blanket.

Which of the two was Rasulullah ﷺ, only then did the people attest.

Abu Bakr ؓ did this because he wanted Rasulullah ﷺ to rest.[73]

At the arrival of Rasulullah ﷺ, the people of Madinah were thrilled.

Rasulullah ﷺ stopped at Quba, where a Masjid they did build.

Originally Yathrib had been Madinah's name.

With the arrival of Rasulullah ﷺ, 'Madinat-un-Nabi' it became.[74]

The Migration of Shu'ayb ar-Rumi ؓ

Shu'ayb ؓ was a poor man, who had come from Rome.

He became wealthy, when in Makkah he set up his home.

The disbelievers of Makkah would not let Shu'ayb ؓ depart,

Unless, from all his hard-earned wealth, he would part.

To be with Rasulullah ﷺ in Madinah, he yearned.

Shu'ayb ؓ readily gave up all that which he had earned.

When the journey to Madinah he made,

Rasulullah ﷺ said to him, *"Fruitful was your trade."*[75]

Intelligence is overrated, wisdom is not.

In Madinah

(Rabi ul-Awal – 1st Year after Hijrah)

Abu Ayyoub's 🕮 Honourable Guest

The Muslims lined the streets; into Madinah, Rasulullah 🕮 made his way.

Every Muslim desired, in their humble homes, Rasulullah 🕮 would stay.

"The camel has been commanded by Allah," Rasulullah 🕮 would say.

He told the people, *"Wherever it stops, that is where I will stay."*

The camel stopped at the place which would be Masjid un-Nabwi's site.

But to make sure of the place, from the camel, Rasulullah 🕮 did not alight.

The camel rose and went further, then back to the same place it did trot.

The people realised the camel had been commanded to stop at this spot.

In this area of Madinah, the Banu Najjar did reside.

They were related to Rasulullah 🕮 from his mother's side.

At the house of Abu Ayyoub Ansari 🕮, Rasulullah 🕮 stayed.

Until his quarters, next to Masjid-e-Nabwi, were made.

The Construction of the Masjid

Where the camel knelt, Rasulullah 🕮 asked who owned the spot.

Two orphans, named Sahl 🕮 and Suhayl 🕮, owned the plot.

They offered the land to Rasulullah 🕮 for free.

But he refused; with them a price he did agree.

To pay the two orphans, arrangements were made.

After which Masjid-e-Nabwi's foundations were laid.

Rasulullah ﷺ did not sit back and make demands,

Rather he helped build the Masjid with his blessed hands.

The Islam of Abdullah bin Salam ﷺ

The people who had migrated were called the Muhajireen.

By the Ansaar, the needs of the Muhajireen were seen.[76]

In Madinah, there lived three tribes of the Jews.[77]

To believe in Rasulullah ﷺ, many of them did refuse.

Abdullah bin Salam ﷺ was their most-learned Rabbi.

He wanted to ascertain whether Rasulullah ﷺ did lie.

To ask Rasulullah ﷺ three questions, he did go.

The answers to these, only a messenger would know.

Abdullah bin Salam 🪑 asked Rasulullah 🪑, "*What is the hour's first sign?*

What is the first thing from which the people of Paradise will dine?"

Regarding how a child will look, a third question was posed.

To Rasulullah 🪑, the answers, Jibra'eel 🪑 had just disclosed.

To the first sign of the hour being a fire, Rasulullah 🪑 did attest,

It would gather all the people, from the east to the west.

In Paradise, fish-liver will be the first thing that people will eat.

The child will look like his mother or father, depending on how they meet.

Abdullah bin Salam 🪑 realised he was a true messenger; Islam, he did embrace.[78]

He told Rasulullah 🪑, "*When the Jews hear about this, my name they will disgrace.*"

Some Jews were called; to the vast knowledge of Abdullah 🪑 they testified.

When they were told of his conversion, about Abdullah's 🪑 status they lied.[79]

Pledges and Pacts

The emigrants had left their homes, wealth and trade behind.

By Rasulullah 🪑, to each Muhajir, an Ansaari brother was assigned.

They would live and treat each other as they would their own brother,

The only difference was they had a different father and mother.

With the Jews, a treaty had also been agreed.

They would help each other at their time of need.

The wronged party would always be aided.

And they would all defend Madinah, if it was raided.

In the City of Madinah, a new enemy arose.

Outwardly as Muslims, the hypocrites would pose.[80]

In reality, they were filled with disbelief.

Their aim was to cause the Muslims grief.

The Battle of Badr

(Ramadhan – 2nd Year after Hijrah)

The Ambush

The Muslims of Makkah were now free,

To worship Allah, in peace and harmony.

The torture and torments, they overcame.

During which their hearts cried Allah's name.

To ambush a Makkan caravan, Muslims were sent.

To Makkah, a fast rider from the caravan went.

In front of the Ka'bah, the rider tore off his shirt.

To make preparations for war, the people, he did exert.

With patience and steadfastness, the Muslims had persevered,

Whilst the disbelievers persecuted them, mocked and jeered.

Now that the Muslims were not in Makkah anymore,

The polytheists were overjoyed at the opportunity for war.

The Muslims had left Madinah, to intercept the caravan.

To have a war with the Makkans was not part of the plan.

To Makkah, Abu Sufyan took a different road.

He had cunningly escaped with the caravan and its load.

The Pagans Prepare for War

The people of Makkah had prepared a large force;
Over a thousand armed men, camels and many a horse.
The majority of them were armed with a shield and a sword.
To wage war against the Muslims, the pagan disbelievers rode.

On the way, from Abu Sufyan, they received a message,
Saying he had escaped; war there was no need to wage.
The army desired to return; to fight there was no longer a need,
But Abu Jahl arrogantly insisted, for war, they should proceed.

The Consultation

Of the army's arrival, Rasulullah ﷺ came to know.
The Muslims realised they needed to prepare for war.
For consultation, the Sahabah were called.
Of the impending war, the Sahabah were told.

Abu Bakr ؓ stood up and was the first one to say,
Any command issued by Rasulullah ﷺ, they would obey.
To give his view, Umar ؓ went ahead,
And reiterated what Abu Bakr ؓ had said.

Al-Miqdad ؓ said, *"Do as Allah directs you to do,*
Proceed, for we are here with you.
What Banu Isra'eel said to Moosa, we will not say.
'You and your Lord fight, here we will stay'."

"Rather we will say, 'You and your Lord go to fight, we will fight with you.'"

Al Miqdad 🕮 further said, to show that to his words he was true,

"By Allah! If you were to take us to Bark al-Ghimad,[81]

We would fight with you, until victory we had."

The men who spoke were Muhajireen; their willingness to fight was clear.

The view of the Ansaar is what Rasulullah 🕮 wanted to hear.

In the Pledge, they promised, 'in Madinah, Rasulullah 🕮 would be defended,'

But they were outside Madinah; Sa'd bin Mu'adh 🕮 realised what was intended.[82]

Sa'd 🕮 said, *"O Messenger of Allah! In you witness we bear.*

And of you having brought us the truth, we all declare.

To obey and sacrifice, a firm oath we all take.

We will willingly do anything, for your sake."

"By the one who sent you with the truth, if you told us to plunge into the sea,

Not one man would stay behind; we would all jump in readily.

We do not fear encountering the enemy, we are experienced in war.

We hope that deeds of valour, which please you, we will be able to show."

The Armies Arrive

Near the village of Badr, the two armies did meet.

Rasulullah 🕮 entreated Allah; *"If the Muslims, the Makkans defeat,*

Then none would be left to worship Allah and pray"[83]

Beseeching victory, in prostration, Rasulullah 🕮 lay.

On the night before the battle was to dawn,

Who would die and where, Rasulullah 🕮 was shown.

The pagans had arrived first, they took the better land,

Whereas the Muslims were walking on soft sand.

Allah caused it to rain; the soft sand, it bound.

The Muslims now stood on firm ground.

The land around the pagans became damp.

They now found it difficult to move around their camp.

The Battle Commences

At the start, single combat was a custom of war.

To challenge each other, the bravest warriors would go.

From the ranks of the pagans, three men rode out.

For someone to challenge them, they did shout.

Three brave men from the Ansaar went out to fight,

The enemy sent them back upon hearing they were Madinite.[84]

From the Quraish, Rasulullah ﷺ sent out his own kin.[85]

The three killed their pagan opponents, they surely did win.

Rasulullah ﷺ sent out Hamzah ؓ, Ubaydah ؓ and Ali ؓ.

They all went against one opponent, it was three against three.

The three pagan men were al-Walid, Utbah and Shaybah.

Hamzah ؓ and Ali ؓ killed their opponents; but they injured Ubaydah ؓ.

Hamzah ؓ and Ali ؓ assisted Ubaydah ؓ; his opponent they did defeat.

They carried Ubaydah ؓ to Rasulullah ﷺ, and lay him by his blessed feet.

Ubaydah ؓ was seriously injured; by Rasulullah ﷺ he passed away.

Ubaydah ibn al-Harith ؓ was the first Muslim to be martyred that day.

The Death of the Pagan Leaders

Two youths came and stood on Abd ur-Rahman bin Awf's ﷺ left and right.

They had heard of Abu Jahl; Abu Jahl they both wanted to fight.

Abd ur-Rahman ﷺ pointed out Abu Jahl; towards him they both ran,

They both struck Abu Jahl, and fatally wounded the evil man.

After the battle, what had happened to Abu Jahl, Rasulullah ﷺ wanted to know.

To look for the Firown of this Ummah, Abdullah bin Masood ﷺ did go.

Abu Jahl was gasping; taking his final breaths, he was lying on the ground,

"Have you seen how Allah disgraced you?" Abdullah ﷺ asked, when he was found.

Abdullah ﷺ stood on his neck; *"I am not disgraced,"* Abu Jahl haughtily replied,

"I am no more than a man, who at the hands of his people, has died.

You have followed difficult ways, you shepherd," Abu Jahl said.

Abdullah ibn Masood ﷺ drew his sword and cut of the tyrant's head.[86]

Abd ur-Rahman bin Awf ﷺ was picking up the left-over stuff,

When he saw an old friend; it was Umayyah bin Khalaf.

He was stood on the battlefield with his son.

They had been defeated; the Muslims had won.

With the capture of Umayyah, Abd ur-Rahman ﷺ realised he would get more,

So the booty, he had collected from the battlefield, he did throw.

He had taken them as captives, when his old master, Bilal ﷺ saw.

To kill Umayyah, the man who had tortured him, Bilal ﷺ swore.

Abd ur-Rahman 🌸 tried to convince Bilal 🌸 that Umayyah was his captive.

But Bilal 🌸 was adamant that this enemy of Islam should not live.

Some Muslims gathered around them; they killed Umayyah's son.

They killed Umayyah too, when Abd ur-Rahman 🌸 told him to run.[87]

Through Allah's clemency and mercy, angels were sent.

To the Muslims, by the angels, a helping hand was lent.

The cursed leaders, which Rasulullah 🌸 had named,

Were found lying dead, after the battle; defamed,

Into a well, the dead leaders of the polytheists were thrown.

Rasulullah 🌸 then asked them, *"Did you find true what Allah had sworn."*

Umar 🌸 asked, *"O Rasulullah, why do you speak to bodies which are dead?"*

"They can hear what I am saying better than you," Rasulullah 🌸 said.

Though the Muslims were weak in number, not well armed,

Allah's promised victory ensured they were not harmed,

Three hundred and thirteen Muslims had bravely fought,

Seventy disbelievers died, and as many were caught.[88]

The Captives

What to do with the captives? The question arose.

Umar ﷺ suggested, they should kill Islam's foes,

To show, with kith and kin, they shared no bond.

Only of Allah, His religion, and His Messenger ﷺ they were fond.

To have captured Abbas ﷺ, an Ansari man claimed,

His capture upon another man, Abbas ﷺ blamed.

"A bald handsome man riding a horse captured me,

Amongst your people this man I cannot see."

"I captured him, O Messenger of Allah," the Ansari did retort.

This was hard to believe; compared to Abbas ﷺ the Ansari was very short.

Rasulullah ﷺ informed him, Allah had sent an angel to give him aid.

For his freedom a heavy ransom, Abbas bin Abdul Muttalib ﷺ paid.

They decided to set the captives free for a ransom,

Some of them taught Muslims, so educated they become.

Money was taken from those captives who could pay.

This was done as some might become Muslim one day.

How stars beautify the dark sky so too does good character beautify man who is enshrouded in the

darkness of his sins.

The Aftermath of Badr

News of the War

At Badr, for a few days, Rasulullah ﷺ did stay.

After which, to Madinah, they made their way.

He sent riders ahead to give glad tidings of the victory.

Some people did not believe, until the captives they did see.

However, there was also grievous news that day,

Rasulullah's ﷺ daughter, Ruqayyah, had passed away.

Those who were in Madinah, had just finished burying her.

When the news of victory, to them, the riders did confer.

A rider arrived, in Makkah, to give them the news,

To the small Muslim army, the pagans did lose.

He named all the chieftains that had been killed.

With anger and remorse, the disbelievers were filled.

Abu Lahab had sent someone to fight in his place.

He was unable to bear the humiliation and disgrace.

Dragging his feet, to the Zamzam tent Abu Lahab went.

Abu Rafi ﷺ was there, carving arrows in the tent.

From Badr, Abu Sufyan bin Haarith bin Abdul Muttalib came.

He was the cousin of Rasulullah ﷺ; Mughira was his real name.

Mughira informed Abu Lahab of how angels had descended,

And how against these angels they were undefended.

Abu Rafi 🌸, who was a Muslim, expressed joy at the angels' role.

When Abu Lahab heard him, his anger went out of control.

He began to hit Abu Rafi 🌸, who was Abbas's 🌸 freed slave.

Abbas's 🌸 wife got angry; with a pole, Abu Lahab's head, she did cave.[89]

She had hit him so hard, it cracked open his head.

The wound became septic; an infection soon spread.

He died from the infection; for three days he was left unburied.

Out of fear of the infection, to go near him people worried.

The dead body of Abu Lahab started to smell.

To bury it, upon his two sons the responsibility fell.

They would catch the infection, they did fear.

The body lay in the house; they wouldn't get near.

Then a man of the Quraish rebuked the two.

He said, *"Come along, with it, I will assist you."*

At the body, from a distance, water they did throw.

Near the dead rotting body they would not go.

In its burial, for a long time they had tarried.

To the upper reaches of Makkah, the corpse they carried.

The placed their father's body next to a wall.

Then they threw stones at him, until they covered him all.

The Assassin

Over the loss of their dear ones, Umair and Safwan bin Umayyah wept.[90]

Umair ibn Wahb fumed, *"I would go kill Muhammad, if it was not for my debt."*

Safwan agreed to take care of his debts and look after his family.

To kill Rasulullah 🌸, in secret, Safwan and Umair did agree.

Poison, on his sword, Umair applied.

Then towards Madinah, he did ride.

Umar ﷺ saw him at the Masjid door,

And asked him what he had come for.

He alleged he had come to enquire of his child's welfare,

Who had been captured in Badr, and was held as a captive there.

Rasulullah ﷺ again enquired from him the real reason why he came.

Each time, the response they received was the same.

The secret meeting with Safwan, then Rasulullah ﷺ disclosed.

Nobody else was present, when the deal had been proposed.

To nobody, this secret, did either of them confide.

In the apostleship of Rasulullah ﷺ, Umair ﷺ testified.[91]

Revenge is a sweet poison pleasing to the soul.

Forgiveness is a bitter pill pleasing to the Lord.

Banu Qaynuqa Break the Treaty

The Honour of a Lady

Banu Qaynuqa was a Jewish tribe which resided in Madinah; one of three.

They had come into an alliance with the Muslims by signing the treaty.

To the Muslims of Madinah, trouble, they started to cause.

The terms of the treaty, they had begun to openly oppose.

One day, the Banu Qaynuqa had gone a step too far.

A Muslim woman went to buy something from their bazaar.

Her garment to her back, one of the Jewish men tied.

She became fully exposed and was unable to hide.

A Muslim who was present went and killed him,

The Jews retaliated and killed that Muslim.

Against the Muslims, the Jews had declared war.

To their forts, with an army, Rasulullah ﷺ did go.

The Siege

Around the forts of the Jews, a siege was laid.

For fifteen days, in their forts the Jews stayed.

Until into their hearts, by Allah, fear was cast.

They surrendered, and waited for judgement to be passed.

The leader of the hypocrites was Abdullah bin Ubay.

"*Due to their alliance with me, let them go,*" he did say.

Rasulullah ﷺ knew, of being Muslim, his testimony was fake.

But acquiescing to his intercession a decision he did make.

Banu Qaynuqa had to surrender their wealth and equipment of war.

Then they were banished; out of Madinah they had to go.

They weren't allowed to ever return to Madinah again.

The booty was then distributed amongst the Muslim men.

*If there is no **unity** in h**uma**nity then all that remains are HMA; High Maintenance Animals.*

The Battle of Uhud

(Shawwal – 3rd Year after Hijrah)

Preparations for War

Over a year had passed, since Badr was fought.

For their defeat at Badr, revenge the pagans sought.

Lying in their graves, their leaders were dead.

To Madinah, an army of three thousand was led.

With hatred for Islam and revenge, hearts were filled,

Especially of those whose relatives and leaders had been killed.

Every disbeliever contributed towards this evil cause.

Once and for all, they wanted to destroy their foes.

Abbas bin Abdul Muttalib ﷺ saw the plans, which the pagans had hatched.

An urgent letter regarding the attack, to Rasulullah ﷺ, he dispatched.

Rasulullah ﷺ gathered the Muhajireen and Ansaar for consultation.

The Sahabah decided, at Rasulullah's ﷺ door, guards they should station.

The Consultation

The Muslims were alert; of the army they were aware.

For an immediate attack, they all did prepare.

About the enemy, scouts would send Rasulullah ﷺ news.

Over where the battle should take place, Rasulullah ﷺ did muse.

Rasulullah ﷺ was of the opinion that in Madinah they should stay.

They would fight from within, whilst out in the open the enemy lay.

Abdullah bin Ubay, the hypocrite, wanted to avoid the fight.

So he agreed with Rasulullah ﷺ, saying his opinion was right.[92]

By many Sahabah, the Battle of Badr was missed.

To prove their valour, to the army, they did enlist.

Showing their courage, out of Madinah they wanted to go.

Against the polytheists, they wanted to wage war.[93]

After Jumu'ah salaah, Rasulullah ﷺ went home; his armour he wore.

Resentment for disagreeing with Rasulullah, ﷺ some Sahabah did show.

To Rasulullah ﷺ, Sa'd bin Mu'adh ؓ and Usaid bin Hudair ؓ went,

And informed him, 'their actions, the Sahabah did resent.'[94]

They apologised, "O Rasulullah, with you we should not disagree,

We will stay in Madinah; to do what you desire, you are free."

"It does not befit a messenger to take his armour off," Rasulullah replied,

"After he had put it on, until between him and the enemy, Allah does decide."

The Zeal of the Young Sahabah

Raf'ee bin Khadeej ؓ was a Sahabi; young in age.

For peace in the land, he wanted to wage.

To give the impression of being tall, on his toes he stood.

Upon seeing his height, to fight, Rasulullah ﷺ said he could.

Sumra 🕊 saw that Raf'ee 🕊 was going to fight.

He claimed that he was stronger in power and might.

Sumra 🕊 wrestled with him and got him on the floor.

So Rasulullah 🕊 gave the youngster permission to go.

At Uhud, the Makkan disbelievers did stop.

And they burnt the Muslims' farms and crop.

In their army, they had three thousand men.

The Muslims were a thousand; short in numbers again.

The Battle Commences

On the seventh of Shawaal, the battle took place.

An army of three thousand, the Muslims did face.

Led by Abdullah bin Ubay, the hypocrites turned back.

Due to which in numbers the Muslims did now lack.[95]

In rows, the army, Rasulullah 🕊 began to array.

On a nearby hillock, he told some archers to stay.

He told them not move, until his command they hear.

Rasulullah 🕊 feared they would be attacked from the rear.[96]

From the ranks of the infidels, Talhah bin Abi Talhah rode out,

He was known for his bravery, for a challenger he did shout.

To fight him, came out from the Muslims ranks, Zubair bin al-Awwam 🕊.[97]

He finished off the man, who was known as 'the Battalion's Ram'.[98]

Fear within the disbelievers could be sensed.

The parties clashed, and the battle commenced.

Every pagan who ran to hold their standard was killed.[99]

Seeing the Muslims winning, in the pagans fear was instilled.

Hanzalah ﷺ was newly married; he had left his wife's bed.

When he heard the call to arms, to the battle he did head.

Into the thick of the battle, Hanzalah ﷺ did dive.

He fought on bravely, but he did not survive.

Khalid bin Waleed tried to attack the Muslims from the rear.[100]

The archers placed on the hillock would not let him near.

The Muslims had gained the upper-hand; the enemy began to retreat.

The pagans knew, the Muslims, they would not be able to defeat.

The Grave Mistake

The archers which were posted to protect the rear

Began to leave their post, thinking victory was near.

They forgot the command; the booty they went to pursue.

This gave an opportunity for the enemy to get through.

The leader of the archers, Abdullah bin Jubair ﷺ, told them not to go.

But forty of the men left, saying they had won the war.

Now Khalid bin Waleed, with his cavalry, saw their chance.

To attack the Muslims' rear, through the pass he did advance.

In tactics, Khalid bin Waleed was very wise,

He attacked from behind, to many Muslims' demise,

Seventy were martyred, due to this blunder,

As the archers had left their post to plunder.

When the fleeing pagans saw Khalid attack,

With a renewed vigour, they all came back.

The Muslims were scattered, thinking they had won.

Towards the advancing pagans, they paid no attention.

The Muslims were confused, but back into battle they did go.

The Muslims were unable to differentiate between friend and foe.

Not knowing who the enemy was, some Muslims killed each other by mistake.[101]

A few Muslims feared for their lives; the battle they did forsake.

The Martyrdom of Hamzah ﷺ

Wah'shi was a slave, whose master was Jubair bin Mut'im.

If Wah'shi killed Hamzah ﷺ, he had promised to free him.[102]

Wah'shi was well-known for his skill with the spear.

He hid behind a rock; waiting for 'the Lion of Allah' to come near.[103]

Hamzah ﷺ had just fought off an enemy; Wah'shi saw his chance.

From behind the rock, towards Hamzah ﷺ, Wah'shi threw his lance.

The spear went through him and from the other side it reappeared.

Hamzah ﷺ had been martyred; by Wah'shi he had been speared.

The Rumour

The standard of the Muslims, by Mus'ab bin Umair ﷺ was held.

He only let it fall after his two hands were cut and he was felled.

The one who had martyred Mus'ab ﷺ was ecstatic and thrilled.

Mus'ab ﷺ resembled Rasulullah ﷺ, so they thought he had been killed.

About Rasulullah's ﷺ death, they spread false news.

To believe in the rumours, Ali ﷺ blatantly did refuse.

He fought bravely, until Rasulullah ﷺ he could see.

Thinking he was dead, from battle some did flee.

The enemy approached Rasulullah ﷺ; Ali ﷺ, he would send.

Single-handedly, the onslaught of men, he would fend.

Anas bin Nadr ﷺ came across some Muslims, who were scared.

Upon hearing Rasulullah ﷺ had died, they had all despaired.

Anas ﷺ told them, "Let us die for what Rasulullah has died for."

Then he advanced to the battlefield, where Sa'd bin Mu'adh ﷺ he saw.

He told Sa'd ﷺ, from Uhud, the fragrance of Paradise he could smell.

He fought the enemy courageously, until he was martyred and fell.

Around Rasulullah ﷺ, only a few Muslims could be found.

They protected him; Rasulullah ﷺ they did surround.

The pagans were merciless in their onslaught.

Around Rasulullah, the Sahabah ﷺ bravely fought.

Rasulullah ﷺ would say, "Who fill fight them back?"

One of the men would step forward and attack.

All these Sahabah were martyred, only two remained.

For protecting Rasulullah ﷺ, Paradise each of them gained.

Sa'd bin Abi Waqqas ؓ and Talhah bin Ubaidullah ؓ were the remaining two.

Rasulullah ﷺ said, "Shoot Sa'd, may my mother and father be sacrificed for you."

Two spikes of a helmet wounded Rasulullah's ﷺ blessed face.

Some of his blessed teeth also broke, of which there was no trace.

Rasulullah ﷺ stumbled; into a hole he did fall.

"Put your blessed head down," Talhah ؓ would call.

He would say, "For your protection, my chest is in the way".

To protect Rasulullah ﷺ, in front of him he did stay.

Towards Rasulullah ﷺ, by the pagans, arrows were hailed.

Through the air, in great numbers arrows sailed.

Talhah ؓ stopped the arrows with his bare arm,

To ensure that Rasulullah ﷺ came to no harm.

Abu Bakr ؓ saw Rasulullah ﷺ; towards him he ran.

Running swiftly alongside him there was another man.

It was the trustworthy one, Abu Ubaydah bin al-Jarrah ؓ.[104]

Searching for Rasulullah ﷺ, he had also seen him from far.

To the wounds of Rasulullah ﷺ, they both wanted to tend.

Due to his insistence, Abu Bakr ؓ let Abu Ubaydah ؓ do it in the end.

In front of Rasulullah ﷺ they saw Talhah ؓ, who from many wounds did bleed,

He said, "See to your brother ,he has earned Paradise through his deed."

The Withdrawal

Towards a group of Muslims, Rasulullah ﷺ and his guards drew near.

Ka'b ibn Malik ؓ recognised him and shouted, *"Rasulullah is here."*

Rasulullah ﷺ told him to stay quiet, as he did not want the pagans to hear.

Some Muslims heard the shout; towards the voice they did steer.

To Mount Uhud, Rasulullah ﷺ and his companions began to withdraw.

Rasulullah ﷺ withdrew with his men, but Ubay bin Khalaf saw.

He was bellowing, *"Where is Muhammad? I will kill him or I will be struck dead."*[105]

The companions asked to go combat him; *"Leave him,"* Rasulullah ﷺ said.

Ubay bin Khalaf began to draw near.

Rasulullah ﷺ readied himself with a spear.

For a spot to strike him, Rasulullah ﷺ did check.

With the spear, he scratched Ubay on his neck.

Ubay fled back to the Quraish; *"Muhammad has killed me,"* he bawled.

Upon seeing the scratch, *"You are afraid of death,"* Ubay they did scold.

"He had already told me, in Makkah, he would kill me," Ubay said,

"By Allah, even if he had just spat on me, I would be dead."[106]

On the way back to Makkah, out of pain he did bawl.

Before he died, he said, *"By the one in whose hand is my soul,*

To the people of Majaz, if the pain I am feeling was distributed,

It would cause them to die.;" after this he was forever muted.

On a hillock, Rasulullah ﷺ came across a rock, he could not ascend.

In front of Rasulullah ﷺ, to make a step to climb up, Talhah ﷺ did bend.

Some pagans tried to follow them and Rasulullah ﷺ they tried to attack.

By the companions of Rasulullah ﷺ, these pagans were driven back.

After this last attempt, back to their camps the pagans retreated.

They took the withdrawal as a sign, that the Muslims were defeated.

They began mutilating the martyred Muslims, which were lying on the ground.

Hind ripped out and chewed the liver of Hamzah ﷺ, when his body she found.[107]

When the disbelievers had made their preparations to leave,

Towards the group of Muslims, Abu Sufyan did weave.

He called out, *"Next year at Badr, we will meet again."*

"Yes we will," called out one of the Muslim men.

On the wounds of Rasulullah ﷺ, water they would pour,

But the water only increased the blood's flow.

To the bleeding of Rasulullah ﷺ, his daughter, Fatimah ﷺ tended.

Only after placing on them a burnt rag, the wounds mended.

Because the archers left their post, and booty they went to find,

They gave the enemy an opportunity to attack from behind.

For the Muslims, this dreadful mistake was of a great cost.

Due to which the nearly won battle was lost.

The Martyrs

Mus'ab bin Umair ﷺ was martyred in this war.[108]

His shroud was too small to cover him from head to toe.

Before Islam a life of luxury and comfort he used to live.

He sacrificed this all for Allah; then his life he also did give.

In the battle in a state of impurity, Hanzalah ﷺ had been.

Water dripping from his body, by the Sahabah was seen.

Rasulullah ﷺ told the companions that angels were giving him a bath.

Hanzalah ﷺ, 'Ghaseel ul-Malaikah', died in Allah's path.[109]

Rasulullah ﷺ was much grieved when he saw his uncle and foster brother.[110]

When Hamzah's ﷺ sister came, he told Zubair ﷺ to stop his mother.[111]

She knew he had been mutilated but insisted his body they show.

Upon seeing her brother, for his forgiveness from Allah, she did implore.

In twos, in their graves the martyrs were laid.

Their funeral salaah, Rasulullah ﷺ prayed.

At Hamzah's ﷺ grave, Rasulullah ﷺ did weep.

The love he had for his uncle ran very deep.

To leave this world we have come, for we were born to die one day.

The Aftermath of Uhud

The Muslims returned to Madinah; they were wounded and tired.

Rasulullah ﷺ worried about the plans, which the pagans may have conspired.

They had not been awarded victory, as they left the battlefield first.[112]

Rasulullah ﷺ feared, for the blood of Muslims, they may still thirst.

The idea of the enemy returning, Rasulullah ﷺ pondered during the night.

The next morning, Rasulullah ﷺ told the Sahabah to prepare to fight.

Only those who had participated in Uhud were allowed to go.

When Abdullah bin Ubay asked for permission, Rasulullah said ﷺ, "No."[113]

At a place called Hamra al-Asad, their camp was set,

Where a man called Ma'bad bin Abi Ma'bad ﷺ, they met.

Regarding yesterday's battle, Rasulullah ﷺ, he addressed.

At the loss of the Muslims, his sorrow he expressed.

Rasulullah ﷺ gave Ma'bad bin Abi Ma'bad ؓ a task.

To overtake Abu Sufyan and his army, he did ask.

To convince Abu Sufyan not to carry out what he did intend,

To the pagan army, Ma'bad bin Abi Ma'bad ؓ , he did send.

Ma'bad bin Abi Ma'bad ؓ arrived not a minute too late;

The Muslims, the pagan army were planning to annihilate.

Ma'bad ؓ told them, 'a large Muslim force was on their tail.'

Upon hearing this news, the pagan army's courage did fail.

After Uhud people thought the Muslims were weak.

To take advantage of the situation, they did seek.

Against the Muslims, neighbouring tribes rebelled.

By the Muslims, all of the uprisings were quelled.

Victory is not the final result, rather the manner in which you react to victory is. For a man is not praised for his defeat, he is praised for how he dealt with and overcame it.

The Betrayal at ar-Raji

Treachery

To Rasulullah ﷺ, the tribes of Udal and Qurah came.

To having converted to Islam, some of their tribe did claim.

They asked Rasulullah ﷺ to send, with them, some men.

Rasulullah ﷺ sent his companion; they numbered ten.

When they reached a place called ar-Raji,

Up a small hillock, the Muslims had to flee.

They had been ambushed by a clan;

A hundred archers from Banu Lihyan.

A pledge to the Muslims, the ambushers proposed.

They would betray them again, Asim ﷺ supposed.

From the hill, the Muslims fought the group bravely,

Until all of them were killed, except for three.

Now the betrayers again called out to the three,

If they came down, their safety they would guarantee.

The three accepted, and came down from high ground.

The disbelievers seized them, and the three were bound.

One Muslim rebuked them for their lie,

And stated that he preferred to die.

So he started to resist them, once again.

For resisting his capture, he was slain.

The Two Captives

Khubaib 🌺 and Zaid bin ad-Dathna 🌺 were the two who survived.

To sell them to the pagans of Makkah, a plan was contrived.

Safwan bin Umayyah killed Zaid 🌺, when he was bought.

Revenge for his father's death at Badr he sought.

Asim 🌺, the leader of the group, had been martyred on the hill.

During the battle of Badr, one of the pagan leaders he did kill.

They sent someone to retrieve his corpse, which had been left discarded.[114]

When he got there he found, by a swarm of hornets, Asim 🌺 was guarded.[115]

As for Khubaib 🌺; for a while, in a house he was tied,

Until to crucify him, the disbelievers did decide.

He was taken out of Haram, to Tan'eem, to be crucified.

To his last request to pray salaah, the pagans complied.[116]

Upon finishing, he said, *"For a long time, I would have prayed,*

But I feared you would think, of death, I was afraid."

On to a tree, Khubaib 🌺 was strung.

Before his death some verses of poetry he sung.

"The confederates have gathered their tribes around me.

They summoned all who would come to see.

They have gathered women and children around.

To a lofty trunk, I am tightly bound."

"To Allah alone, do I complain,

Of my helplessness and pain.

And of the death that is to be,

The confederates have prepared me."

"Lord of the Throne, give me patience against what they have contrived,

They have cut my flesh bit by bit, and from food I have been deprived.

They let me choose infidelity, but death to me is more dear.

Tears roll out of my eyes, but not out of fear."

"By Allah, I do not fear if I die a Muslim," he did call,

"For the sake of Allah, on which side my body does fall.

I will not show subservience to the enemy.

If my Lord wishes, in my torn limbs and broken joints, He will bless me."

Abu Sufyan remarked, "Do you not wish Muhammad was in your place instead.

Whilst you were with your family, and we cut of Muhammad's head?"

Khubaib ﷺ replied, "By Allah, I do not wish Muhammad was here instead of me,

Or that he is pricked by a thorn, whilst I am sitting with my family."[117]

The Quraish then told Uqbah to crucify him.

They appointed someone to guard this devout Muslim.

Amr bin Umayyah stole his body during the night.

He took Khubaib ﷺ away, and buried him out of sight.

The value of all humans is equal in death. Why then is the value of all human life not considered equal?

Massacre at Ma'una

A man came to Madinah, whose name was Abu Barra.

He was asked to embrace Islam, by Rasulullah ﷺ.

He said, *"To call to Islam, send your men to the people of Najd."*

He feared for their lives; to send them he begrudged.

Only when Abu Bara promised to protect them, did he consent.

To the people of Najd, seventy very learned Sahabah went.

They travelled together, until they reached Ma'una's well.

Here, to send a message to Amir bin Tufail, Rasulullah ﷺ did tell.[118]

To Amir they sent Rasulullah's ﷺ message with Haram bin Milhan ﷺ.

Amir did not listen to the message; to spear Haram ﷺ, he ordered a man.

When Haram ﷺ saw his blood; the result of what Amir had done,

He exclaimed, *"Allahu Akbar! By the Lord of the Ka'bah, I have won."*

Amir tried to rouse Banu Amir to fight the Muslims; but he was spurned.

The Muslims were under Abu Bara's protection; so to Banu Sulaym he turned.[119]

To fight against the Muslims, Banu Sulaym accepted his call.

They surrounded the Muslims, and fought until all, but one Muslim, did fall.[120]

Two Sahabah were left to look after the animals; they saw birds in the air.

Realising there was a battle they ran to it; in the reward they wanted to share.[121]

Al-Mundhir ﷺ was killed but Amr bin Umayyah ﷺ was taken captive.

Amir's mother had pledged to free a slave, so he let Amr ﷺ live.[122]

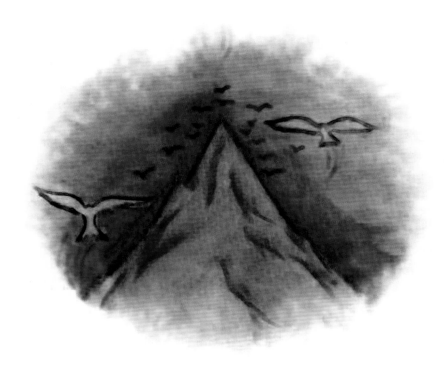

Returning to Madinah, Amr saw two men resting under a tree, from Bani Kilab.

He wanted to avenge his dead companions; the two men, Amr ﷺ did stab.

He told Rasulullah ﷺ what happened, and of the two murdered men that laid.

Banu Kilab were under Rasulullah ﷺ protection; so their blood money was paid.

By revelation what had happened, Rasulullah ﷺ came to know.

He was greatly grieved, and felt much pain and sorrow.

For many days, during every Fajr salaah which Rasulullah ﷺ prayed,[123]

Against those who were responsible, a prayer he made.

How stars beautify the dark sky so too does good character beautify man who is enshrouded in the
darkness of his sins.

The Expulsion of Banu Nadeer

Banu Nadeer were a Jewish tribe; the treaty they had signed.[124]

They started to violate the terms; to the Muslims they were unkind.

Part of the agreement was to contribute to blood money owed.

To collect their share of the blood money, Rasulullah ﷺ went to their abode.

It was for the two men of Banu Kilab who Amr had killed by mistake.

They told Rasulullah ﷺ to sit under a wall, whilst to get the money they did fake.

They planned to crush Rasulullah ﷺ from on top of the wall with a large stone.

Jibra'eel ﷺ came to him; of the evil intentions of Banu Nadeer, he did warn.

Rasulullah ﷺ quickly stood up; to Madinah he went.

To Banu Nadeer, an order to evacuate was sent.

They were given a time span of ten days to depart.

Or from their bodies, their heads will be made to part.

To Rasulullah's ﷺ threat, Abdullah bin Ubay told Banu Nadeer not to pay heed.

The hypocrite agreed to come to their aid, with his men, when they were in need.

Their leader replied, *"We will not leave our houses, do whatever you want to do."*

They relied on the support of Abdullah bin Ubay; thinking he would be true.

When Rasulullah ﷺ received Huyay's reply, "*Allahu Akbar,*" he did shout.[125]

Towards the forts of Banu Nadeer, Rasulullah ﷺ and his Sahabah set out.

For many days, the Muslim army laid a siege around their fort.

To shooting arrows and pelting stones, Banu Nadeer did resort.

Banu Nadeer realised ibn Ubay was not going to come at their time of need.

To evacuate Madinah on the terms of Rasulullah ﷺ, they finally agreed.

To take with them what they could carry, they made a request.

Except for weapons, they took everything that they possessed.

It is the height of foolishness of the foolish one to question the wisdom of the wise.

Badr ~ The Appointment

(Sha'ban – 4th Year after Hijrah)

After Uhud, which the pagans counted as the Muslims defeat,

The Muslims had agreed with the pagans, again at Badr, they would meet.

A year later at Badr, for their enemy to arrive, the Muslims did wait.

They anticipated their arrival for many days; approximately eight.

Abu Sufyan had set out with an army of over two thousand men.

Fearing the consequences of the fight, they went back to Makkah again.

About the hardships they might face that year, excuses he made.

The army was also afraid of the encounter; they all willingly obeyed.

Though death is inevitable, youth seems eternal.

The Reconnaissance of

Doumat ul-Jandal

(Rabi ul-Awwal – 5th Year after Hijrah)

On the Syrian border, there were men who would plunder and raid.

Plans to attack and rob Madinah, these highway men had made.

To take precautionary measures, Rasulullah ﷺ did decide.

He set off towards them instead; he took with him a guide.

To surprise them, they travelled by night and rested in the day.

When they reached Doumat ul-Jandal, the enemy had run away.

The Muslims captured the left behind shepherds and cattle.

They could not find the enemy; they had fled before the battle.

To fight the Muslims, the Makkan pagans could not brave.

The Jews and hypocrites, in Madinah, had started to behave.

Now that all the threats had been subdued,

Their aim of spreading Islam, the Muslims pursued.

Ilm (knowledge) is an everlasting candle which does not benefit unless lit with the flame of aml (acting upon it).

The Invasion of the

Confederates

(Zhu al-Qa'dah – 5th Year after Hijrah)

The Alliance of the Confederates

The Jews of Banu Nadeer had been made to evacuate.

For Islam and Rasulullah ﷺ, they were full of hate.

They wanted the Muslims destroyed, once and for all.

Too cowardly to do it themselves, upon the pagans they did call.

The Jews and the pagans rallied more tribes towards their cause.

Many tribes of Arabia gathered to destroy the Muslims; their foes.

To meet at Madinah at an appointed time, they all did plan.

There were over ten thousand men; their leader was Abu Sufyan.

The Trench

Of the preparations which had been made, Rasulullah ﷺ got word.

He gathered his companions and with them he conferred.

To dig a trench around Madinah was, the Persian, Salman's ﷺ view.

When they were besieged, that is what the Persians used to do.

Upon his opinion, they unanimously agreed.

They began digging a trench, with great speed.

Whilst digging, the Sahabah were famished and tired.

During the days of digging, a few miracles transpired.

The Sahabah came across a boulder, which they could not break.

They approached Rasulullah ﷺ, and asked what course of action to take.

His way to the trench, which had the hard boulder, Rasulullah ﷺ made.

He climbed down into the trench, and struck the boulder with a spade.

On the first strike, he said, *"Allahu Akbar, the keys of Sham are for me.*

I swear by Allah, the palaces of Sham, I can see."

On the second strike, he said, *"Allahu Akbar, Persia is for me.*

I swear by Allah, now the white palace of Mada'in, I can see."

The third time, he said, *"Allahu Akbar, the keys of Yemen have been given to me.*

I swear by Allah, while I am in my place, the gates of San'a, I can see."

All the Sahabah who tried to break the rock were unable to do so.

With the third strike, from Rasulullah ﷺ, the boulder was no more.[126]

The Famished Army

To see Rasulullah ﷺ famished, Jabir bin Abdullah ﷺ could not bear.

He went home to his wife, and asked what food they had to spare.

She replied, *"A little goat and some barley is all we have got."*

She ground the barley, whilst he slaughtered the goat and put it in a pot.

"Do not disgrace me, in front of Rasulullah," his wife said.

The food would run short, she did dread.

Quietly regarding the food, with Rasulullah ﷺ, Jabir ﷺ did parley.

He told Rasulullah ﷺ of the small goat and the ground barley.

Rasulullah ﷺ called out loudly, *"Jabir has prepared a meal, so let us go."*

He told Jabir ؓ not to take the pot off the fire nor bake the dough.

Jabir's ؓ wife rebuked him, when he told her all the Sahabah had come along.

Rasulullah ﷺ told the hungry Sahabah, *"Enter, and do not throng."*

Rasulullah ﷺ would cut some bread, and on it he would put meat.

He kept on doing so; to their fill, all the Sahabah did eat.

Even after all of those present had eaten, food still remained.

"Eat, and give to others who are also hungry," Rasulullah ﷺ explained.

The Siege

After many days of digging, the trench was finally finished.

When the enemy arrived, their hopes of an easy victory diminished.

For the army of ten thousand to cross the trench was very hard.

On the other side of the trench, three thousand Muslims stood guard.

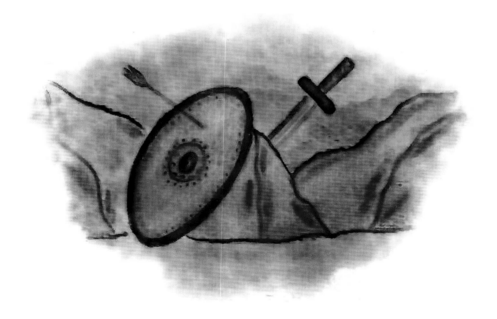

When the enemy drew near, arrows the Muslims would shoot.

A way to infiltrate the Muslims, they desperately looked for a route.

Amr bin Abd Wudd, Ikramah and Dirar managed to get to the other side.

Ikramah bin Abi Jahl and Dirar fled when, at the hands of Ali ﷺ, Amr died.[127]

Umar ﷺ told Rasulullah ﷺ, 'he had not prayed Asr, and the sun had set.'[128]

Rasulullah ﷺ replied, *"By Allah, I have not offered the prayer yet."*

For being distracted from Asr, the disbelievers he did condemn.

He was so furious that he invoked the wrath of Allah upon them.[129]

Enemy in the Camp

In Madinah, the Jewish tribe, Banu Qurayzah still resided.

So far to the treaty with Rasulullah ﷺ, they had abided.

Huyay went to the chief of Banu Qurayzah; Ka'b he tried to incite.[130]

From within Madinah, the Muslims Banu Qurayzah should fight.

At first, the persuasive attempts of Huyay were resisted.

The help of Banu Qurayzah, he finally enlisted.

Somehow, Rasulullah ﷺ got the dreadful news,

That the enemy had enlisted the help of the Jews.

In garrisons, the Muslim women and children were housed.

Outside, by the movement of a Jew, Safiyyah ﷺ was roused.

Hassan bin Thabit ﷺ was garrisoned in the same site.

Safiyyah ﷺ told him to go; the Jew he should fight.

He was unable to do so, is what Hassan ﷺ said.

Safiyyah ﷺ went out; she struck the Jew dead.

The Jews assumed, with fighters, the garrisons were fortified.

To directly attack these garrisons, they no longer tried.

Now they were vulnerable from the front and behind.

A solution to resolve the matter, the Muslims tried to find.

An opportunity to dishearten the Muslims, the hypocrites saw.

Saying they had to protect their homes, they began to withdraw.[131]

Rasulullah's ﷺ Proposal

To cause dissension amongst the enemy, Rasulullah ﷺ came up with a plan.

For their withdrawal, he would offer a third of Madinah's crop to Ghatfan.

With regards to this, the advice of his chief companions, he sought.

He asked Sa'd bin Mu'adh ﷺ and Sa'd bin Ubadah ﷺ what they thought.[132]

"O Rasulullah, if it is Allah's command, then we readily obey,

If it is for our security, we do not need it," they did say.

"Now that we have been honoured with Islam, by our Lord,

The best course of action is to put them to the sword."

Sa'd bin Mu'adh's ﷺ Prayer

Sa'd bin Mu'adh ﷺ was fatally wounded; against the pagans he wanted to strive.

If more fighting was still to happen, he prayed to Allah to keep him alive.

He also prayed to live until revenge against Banu Qurayzah was taken.[133]

The Muslims, at their hour of need, the treacherous tribe had forsaken.

Nu'aym bin Masood's ﷺ Cunning Plan

Nu'aym ﷺ was from Ghatfan; his Islam to Rasulullah ﷺ, he did profess.

He asked him for permission to help the Muslims in their current distress.

He went to Banu Qurayzah; hostages from the Quraish, he told them take,

If the Quraish lost or fled, then Banu Qurayzah they will readily forsake.

He went to the Quraish and alleged that their actions Banu Qurayzah did regret,

To make up for their abandonment, with the Muslims they had met.

They have promised to hand Quraishi hostages to them, Nu'aym ﷺ reported.

To not send the Jews any hostages, the Quraish, he strongly exhorted.

Thus the Quraish told Banu Qurayzah, 'the Muslims they must fight.'

Banu Qurayzah asked for hostages; the Quraish thought Nu'aym ﷺ was right.

Banu Qurayzah were worried what would happen if the Quraish decided to flee.

To give the Muslims hostages, the Quraish thought Banu Qurayzah did agree.

When the Quraish refused to give hostages as a guarantee,

The truth in Nu'aym's ﷺ words the Banu Qurayzah did see.

Nu'aym's ﷺ clever scheme proved to be a success.

The distrust in the enemy ranks caused much distress.[134]

The Spy in the Dark

Rasulullah ﷺ prayed to Allah for the enemy to be defeated.

The enemy was weary; their patience had depleted.

One night, about the enemies plans, Rasulullah ﷺ wanted to know.

To the enemy camp, Rasulullah ﷺ asked for a Sahabi ﷺ to go.

Around all of Madinah, a fierce storm bellowed and raged.

For many days, against the Confederates, war had been waged.

The Sahabah were cold, famished and weak; nobody volunteered for the task.

None of them felt they had the strength to do what Rasulullah ﷺ did ask.

By Rasulullah ﷺ, Huzhaifah ibn al-Yaman ؓ was called.

To infiltrate the enemy camp, he was told.

The plans of the enemy, he was asked to glean.

And he should avoid doing anything which would get him seen.

"O Allah, protect him from in front of him and behind him," Rasulullah ﷺ prayed,

"And from his right and his left and from above and below;" is the prayer he made.

The prayer had just finished, and Allah took Huzhaifah's ؓ cold and fear away.

Clad in a simple garment, to the enemy's camp, Huzhaifah ؓ made his way.

Abu Sufyan wanted to address his army but feared amongst them there was a spy.

It was too dark to see who was who; to catch him, Abu Sufyan did try.

He told the army, the name of their neighbour, they should learn.

He hoped, the spy, this plan would allow him to discern.

Before Huzhaifah ؓ could be asked, he grabbed the nearest man's hand,

"Tell me who you are?" from his neighbour he did demand.

He told him who he was; Huzhaifah ؓ was from amongst them, he thought.

He didn't think to ask Huzhaifah ؓ; he had avoided getting caught.

It was a cold windy night; away the enemy tents had been blown.

Their pots and other equipment, the wind had overthrown.

The howling wind would not allow any fires to burn.

Abu Sufyan told the army that they should all return.

Abu Sufyan mounted his camel; an opportunity, Huzhaifah ﷺ saw.

He could kill their leader; an arrow from his quiver, he did draw.

But then he remembered what Rasulullah ﷺ did say.

To avoid being seen he put his bow and arrow away.

The army was preparing to leave; Huzhaifah ﷺ had learned.

He had accomplished his task; back to Rasulullah ﷺ he returned.

He told Rasulullah ﷺ that the enemy were making plans to leave.

Allah alone foiled the plans of the clans who did disbelieve.

Fulfilling your needs will satiate you, whilst fulfilling your desires will make you hungrier.

The Siege of Banu Qurayzah

The Muslims March Again

The disbelievers had fled from the trench, having earned Allah's wrath.

Rasulullah ﷺ returned home; he laid down his arms, and had a bath.

Jibra'eel عليه السلام came and told him, the angels had not yet put their weapons down.

He told Rasulullah ﷺ to set out, and pointed towards Banu Qurayzah's town.

To regroup, to the tired and cold army, a message was sent.

Towards the township of Banu Qurayzah, the Muslims went.

Whilst going to Banu Qurayzah, the saalah of Asr was due on the way.

Some prayed it on the journey; whilst upon reaching them, Asr, others did pray.

For twenty five days, around their town, a siege was laid.

Three offers to his people, Ka'b bin Asad made.

Either accept Islam, of whose truth from their books was known,

If they did this their families and wealth would be left alone.

Or their families, with their own hands they could smite,

Then Rasulullah ﷺ and his companions they could challenge to fight.

Or on their day of Sabbath, they could attack the Muslims by surprise.[135]

But the people of Banu Qurayzah did not accept any of his advice.

With some Muslims, the Banu Qurayzah had maintained good ties.

They called upon Abu Lubabah ﷺ to ask him for his advice.

They asked him with regards to what would be their fate.

Abu Lubabah ﷺ pointed to his throat; indicating for them death did await.

The trust of Rasulullah ﷺ, Abu Lubabah ﷺ realised he had betrayed.[136]

He went and tied himself to a pillar in the Masjid; there he stayed.

Nobody except Rasulullah ﷺ would untie him from the pillar he swore.

Rasulullah ﷺ said, *"Had he requested me, for his forgiveness, I would have asked for."*

Sa'd's Judgement

To the judgement of Rasulullah ﷺ, the Jews finally decided to comply.

To get some leniency for them, their pre-Islamic ally, Banu Aws, did try.

To the verdict of their leader, Sa'd bin Mu'adh ﷺ, they all did happily accede.

Sa'd ﷺ was called; to whatever judgment he made, Banu Qurayzah had agreed.[137]

In the Battle of the Trench, Sa'd ﷺ had been fatally wounded with an arrow.

To live until retribution was taken against Banu Qurayzah, he had prayed for.

The arrow had struck a main artery, from which blood flowed.

Towards Banu Qurayzah, on a donkey, Sa'd bin Mu'adh ﷺ rode.

Sa'd ﷺ gave his judgement; to kill all the able-bodied males, he decided.

Between the Muslims, the women, children and wealth should be divided.

Only one Jewish women was killed, as she had killed a Muslim.

The Jewish woman had flung a grinding stone at him.

A tent had been placed in the Masjid for Sa'd ﷺ; his situation was dire.

Rasulullah ﷺ wanted to have access to him, so of his health he could enquire.

Due to his severe bleeding, in this tent, Sa'd ﷺ took his last breath.[138]

Rasulullah ﷺ said, *"The throne of the Compassionate One shook on his death."*

Abu Lubabah was still tied to the pillar, due to his accidental crime.

The people would only untie him when it was prayer time.

Allah revealed verses; regarding Abu Lubabah's ﷺ forgiveness, they consisted.

When people rushed to untie him, *'Only Rasulullah will untie me,'* he insisted.

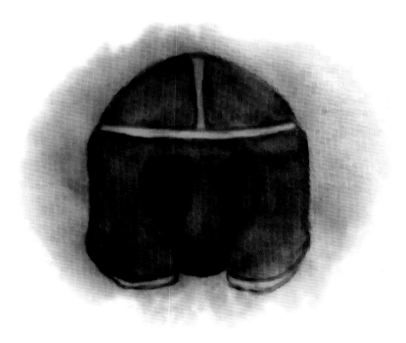

He who considers deception as an art has in reality deceived himself.

The Treaty of Hudaybiyah

(Zhu al-Qa'dah – 6th Year after Hijrah)

The Muslims Proceed for Umrah

One night, in a dream, Rasulullah ﷺ saw,

To do the Umrah with his companions, he did go.

To the companions, the dream was related.

His intention to go for Umrah, he stated.

Towards Makkah, Rasulullah ﷺ and fifteen hundred Muslims rode.

They wore their ihram; they had come in peace, they showed.[139]

After years of exile, to do Umrah, the Muslims had flocked.

But when they reached Hudaybiyah, they found their road was blocked.

A Leader like No Other

The Quraish sent a delegation, to ask what they had come for.

Rasulullah ﷺ told them that they came for Umrah, not for war.

To stop them from Umrah, the Quraish had no right.

If they were barred, the Sahabah were ready to fight.

Urwah went to the Quraish, and related to them what he had seen.[140]

"To the kingdom of Chosroe, Caesar and Negus I have been.

A king with his people, like Muhammad is with his companions, I have not found.

When he performs ablution, they do not allow the used water to touch the ground."

"They rub their faces with that which he does expectorate.

When he speaks, they lower their voices, and quietly wait.

In any situation, this man they will not leave.

His offer is reasonable; do what you conceive."

The Pledge under the Tree

With the Muslims, the Quraish decided to negotiate.

With regards to the terms, there was much debate.

Rasulullah ﷺ desired that Umar ؓ go to the chiefs of Makkah, to speak.

Umar ؓ said, due to his enmity with them, another man he should seek.

Uthman bin Affan ؓ, who had a powerful family in Makkah, was chosen to go.

Uthman ؓ went to Makkah; he told their leaders that they had not come for war.

After they had performed the Umrah, they would leave peacefully.

The Quraish were adamant that they would not let this be.

When the Quraish suggested to Uthman ؓ to do Umrah, he replied,

"How can I perform Umrah, when Rasulullah is denied?"

The delay in Uthman's ؓ return, filled the Muslims with dread.

Regarding the martyrdom of Uthman ؓ, rumours began to spread.

At the hands of Rasulullah ﷺ, the companions swore a pledge, under a tree.

To give their lives, to avenge Uthman's ؓ death, they all did agree.

By Rasulullah ﷺ, with his other hand, for Uthman ؓ this pledge was also sworn.

Allah was very pleased with them; as 'Bay'at ur-Ridwan' it became known.[141]

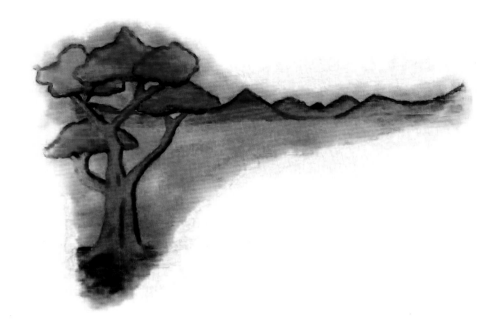

The Treaty is Concluded

The Quraish saw, the Muslims would not cease from what they intend.

To conclude a treaty of peace, with them, some people they sent.

For the Muslims, the terms of the treaty seemed very unfair.

For not being able to do Umrah, many Muslims did despair.

The treaty stated, the Muslims would have to go back today.

They could return next year, and for three days they could stay.

For ten years, against each other, they would not wage war.

Whoever wanted to ally themselves with either party could do so.

Any tribe, which was in alliance with either of them, they could not attack.[142]

Any Quraishi, who fled to the Muslims, would have to be sent back.

Whereas, to the Quraish in Makkah, if any Muslim went,

Back to the Muslims, the renegade would not be sent.

The Day of Abu Jandal 🕌

With Suhayl bin Amr, the treaty Rasulullah 🕌 did agree.

From Makkah, Abu Jandal ibn Suhayl ibn Amr 🕌 broke free.

For being a Muslim, by the pagans, he had been chained.

Of his plight to Rasulullah 🕌 and the Muslims, he complained.

Upon learning of the Muslims arrival, Abu Jandal 🕌 had escaped from the city.

Seeing his state, Rasulullah 🕌 and the companions were moved with pity.

Suhayl remarked, "An opportunity has come, to prove you are faithful to the contract."

Rasulullah 🕌 said, "When your son came to the camp, we had not yet signed the pact."

"But the terms of the treaty had been agreed upon," Suhayl replied.

"Are you going to send me back to the pagans?" Abu Jandal 🕌 cried.

Seeing Abu Jandal 🕌 in this state, the Sahabah were unable to bear.

They were also livid about the treaty, because it was unfair.

With sympathy for Abu Jandal 🕌, Rasulullah's 🕌 heart welled.

But at all costs, the terms of the treaty had to be upheld.

For help from the Muslims, Abu Jandal 🕌 did plead and whine.

Rasulullah 🕌 encouraged him to be patient; to Allah's will, he should resign.

Rasulullah 🕌 informed him, in the name of Allah, a pledge they did take.

Under any circumstance, the terms of the treaty, they could not break.

Rasulullah 🕌 and his companions, this whole situation pained,

As they watched Abu Jandal 🕌 being dragged back to be chained.

To sacrifice their animals, the Sahabah, he addressed.

To do anything, the Sahabah were too depressed.

The Sahabah were furious at the terms; they were not in a good mood.

Rasulullah ﷺ went to his wife; he related to her, the Sahabah's attitude.

'Sacrifice your animal, and shave your head first,' Umm Salamah ﷺ advised.

When the Sahabah saw Rasulullah ﷺ doing it, their animals they too sacrificed.

On the journey home, Surah Fat'h, which said this was a victory, was revealed.[143]

How this would be a manifest victory, to the Sahabah was still concealed.

Patience makes the life sweeter, for moments plucked before their time will taste bitter.

The Manifest Victory

Through the treaty, the Muslims had earned a manifest victory,

The companions of Rasulullah ﷺ were now able to see.

With no fear of war, to spread Islam they were free.

This was the manifest victory, they did not foresee.

Now that all military expeditions, against the Quraish, had ceased,

The number of people accepting Islam greatly increased.

They went to areas of Arabia, which they had been unable to explore.

To propagate Islam, to those tribes, the companions did go.

The Captives Escape

Abu Baseer ﷺ had escaped to Madinah, he came as a Muslim.

The Quraish sent two delegates to Rasulullah ﷺ. asking to return him.

As per the agreement, Rasulullah ﷺ had no choice but to send him back.

On the way to Makkah, Abu Baseer ﷺ killed one of them in an attack.

With Abu Baseer ﷺ on his tail, back to Madinah the other delegate fled.

They reached Rasulullah ﷺ; *"Your obligation is over,"* Abu Baseer ﷺ said,

"Allah has freed you from it, as you handed me over to the men."

But Rasulullah ﷺ had no choice but to hand him over again.

Realising he would be handed over, from Madinah he fled.

To a faraway place, called Saif al-Bahr, Abu Baseer ﷺ did head.

Abu Jandal ﷺ and other Muslims escaped, and joined Abu Baseer ﷺ.

They had become a large group, whom the Quraish began to fear.

They sought revenge against the Quraish; from their caravans, they stole.

They were not part of the treaty; over them, Quraish had no control.

The Quraish went to Madinah; to revoke this term, they did implore.

Madinah was now open to them; so the group of Muslims were sent for.

When the letter arrived, Abu Baseer ﷺ was on his death bed.

After reading the letter, he placed it on his eyes and his head.

He would not return to Madinah; in Saif al-Bahr he died.

They buried him, and then towards Madinah the rest did ride.

Though one may turn a blind eye, it does not mean he is blind.

Propagating Islam

Rasulullah ﷺ was unable to read or write.[144]

The kings, to Islam, he wanted to invite.

To write his letters, he used to have scribes.

He sent letters and delegations to many tribes.

Some of the kings, like Negus, realised Rasulullah ﷺ was right.

They accepted the religion, towards which he did invite.

Some realised he was true, but to believe they did refuse.

Their kingdom, these leaders feared they would lose.

There were others who called Rasulullah ﷺ a liar.

To annihilate this religion, these leaders did conspire.

But their plans were futile against what Allah had planned.

With the help of Allah, Islam had the upper-hand.

The truth of Rasulullah's ﷺ call, people began to see.

They realised, in Islam, there was great beauty.

They saw in it love, peace and brotherhood,

And how it called people towards good.

To call people towards Islam, the Muslims tried.

Due to which, the number of Muslims multiplied.

There were more Muslims than ever before.

Islam, the exiled Jews still did deplore.

The Conquest of Khaybar

(Muharram – 7th Year after Hijrah)

Pre-emptive Measures

The Jew's mischief, Rasulullah ﷺ wanted to prevent.

With an army, to their stronghold in Khaybar, he went.

Ibn Ubay informed the Jews of Rasulullah's ﷺ plan.

The Jews sent a message, requesting help from Ghatfan.

Of Ghatfan coming to their aid, Rasulullah ﷺ got news.

He stopped at a place between Ghatfan and the Jews.

Due to the manoeuvre which Rasulullah ﷺ did devise,

Ghatfan were unable to assist the Jews, their allies.

The army arrived at Khaybar, in the morning; at sunrise.

The Jews had come out to work, with their supplies.

"Muhammad is here with his force," they cried in surprise,

To take refuge in their forts, they thought it was wise.

The Forts Fall

The Jews had many forts, in which they did reside.

In their separate forts, the Jews went to hide.

The Muslim army decided to lay siege to one fort.

To fight the Muslims, the inhabitants did resort.

Those Jews lost the fight; as their fort fell,

They fled to another fort, in which others did dwell.

The forts fell one by one; the Jews began to lose hope.

They realised, to the attacks, they were unable to cope.

One of the Jewish forts gave a really good fight.

The Muslims could not defeat it, with all of their might.

Rasulullah ﷺ said, "I will give this flag, in the morning,

To a man by whose hand, victory, Allah will bring."

He said, "He loves Allah and his Rasul, and Allah and his Rasul love him."

To be given the banner to hold, it was the desire of every Muslim.

In the morning all the Muslims had gathered; they were all waiting eagerly.

Rasulullah ﷺ came out; he asked regarding the whereabouts of Ali ﷜.

Rasulullah ﷺ sent for Ali ﷜; he was told Ali ﷜ had a severe pain in his eye.

Ali ﷜ was brought forth; saliva on his eye his blessed, Rasulullah ﷺ did apply.

Ali's ﷜ eye became such, as though it had not pained him before.

With the flag in his hand, towards the yet undefeated fort, he did go.

The forts began to fall; the Jews decided to negotiate,

Before they were defeated, and it was too late.

By Rasulullah ﷺ, a deal with the Jews was signed.

Khaybar and their wealth, the Jews were ordered to leave behind.

All of the Jews wealth, the Muslims did take.

The farms of Khaybar, the Jews could not forsake.

Rasulullah ﷺ allowed the defeated Jews to stay there,

On the condition that half of the crops, with the Muslims, they share.

The Dream of Safiyyah ﷺ

Huyay bin Akhtab had a daughter; Safiyyah ﷺ was her name.

She had dreamt a dream before the Muslims came.

In her dream she saw a moon had fallen into her lap.

She told her husband of the dream; he gave a hard slap.

Her husband Kinanah ibn al-Rabi was furious at what she had seen,

"You wish for Muhammad," he fumed; that is what the dream did mean.

Her husband and father died in the battle, which was fought.

Safiyyah bint Huyay ﷺ was taken as a captive, when she was caught.

Rasulullah ﷺ took her as his wife, after setting her free.

The mark of the slap, on her face, Rasulullah ﷺ did see.

Upon enquiring, she narrated to him the dream of the moon.[145]

Her noble lineage went back to the Messenger Haroon ﷺ.

The Poisoned Sheep

After the battle of Khaybar had been fought,

By a Jewish woman, a cooked sheep was brought.

She had poisoned the sheep, which was going to be fed.

To avenge her family, she wanted Rasulullah ﷺ dead.

From the poisoned shoulder of the sheep, Rasulullah ﷺ did eat.

It was poisoned, he was informed by the shoulder of meat.

"Take your hands away," the Sahabah were told.

For the Jewish woman, Rasulullah ﷺ called.

"Did you poison this sheep?" he asked the Jew.

The Jewish woman exclaimed, *"Who told you?"*

Rasulullah ﷺ told her, he was informed by the meat in his hand.

He asked her what she had intended, with what she planned.

She replied, *"It would not have harmed you, if you are a messenger true,*

And if you are not a messenger, then we would have got rid of you."

Rasulullah ﷺ forgave her; but a Sahabi died who had partaken from the meal.

At the time of his death, the effect of the poison, Rasulullah ﷺ did also feel.[146]

After the victory at Khaybar, towards Madinah the Muslims turned.

They found that the remaining migrants from Abyssinia had returned.

Rasulullah ﷺ embraced Ja'far ibn Abi Talib ﷺ and kissed him on his forehead.

"I don't know which is more pleasing, Ja'far's return or the victory of Khaybar," he said.

One man's kindness to another man is what makes us mankind.

The Expedition of Rags

(7th Year after Hijrah)

The Highway Robbers

Most of the hostile parties of Arabia had been subdued.

Riots and robbery, the Bedouins of Najd still pursued.

To put this under control, Rasulullah ﷺ did intend.

He went, with an army, to put their rebellion to an end.

Their camels, between them, the Muslims did divide.

They had to take turns for everyone to ride.

The Muslims had to walk, as transportation was less.

With rags, their wounded feet, they did dress.

The Best of Men

Under the shade of a tree, to rest, Rasulullah ﷺ had laid.

The Sahabah had dispersed, in search of shade.

Rasulullah ﷺ hung his sword on a branch of the tree.

A Bedouin approached, and took the sword quietly.

Rasulullah ﷺ awoke to find the man standing by the tree.

Brandishing the sword, he said, *"Who will save you from me?"*

The man dropped the sword when *"Allah,"* Rasulullah ﷺ replied.

When Rasulullah ﷺ picked it up; *"You are the best of men,"* the man cried.

Rasulullah ﷺ asked him to embrace Islam, but the Bedouin did not agree.

He said that he would never fight Muslims; so Rasulullah ﷺ set him free.

Though Rasulullah's ﷺ offer to accept Islam the man had spurned,

"I have seen the best of all people," he said to his tribe, when he returned.

Sincere Observance of Prayer

A pagan woman had been taken captive, during the war.

To shed the blood of a Muslim, her husband swore.

He secretly approached the Muslim camp, at night.

A guard standing watch, he though he did sight.

He shot an arrow at him, but the guard continued to stand.

On the stationed guard, a few more arrows, he did land.

The guard was Abbad bin Bishr ﷺ, in prayer he was immersed.

He did not react to being shot; he wanted to finish his prayer first.

The Matter Resolved

The Bedouins at the hands of the Muslims did fall,

After which their situation came under control.

The Muslims managed to reconcile matters with Ghatfan.

Many people embraced Islam in this short time-span.

He who considers deception as an art has in reality deceived himself.

The Umrah

(Zhu al-Qadah – 7th Year after Hijrah)

Since the treaty of Hudaybiyah, a year had passed.

To go for Umrah, two thousand Muslims had amassed.

To enter Makkah and to visit the Ka'bah, the Muslims were free.

To allow them to do Umrah this year, the Quraish did agree.

According to the treaty, they were only allowed to take a sheathed sword.

But Rasulullah ﷺ feared that the Quraish would try to spread discord.

He had a platoon of men mobilized, who were all well-armed.

This was done to ensure that the Muslims were not harmed.

From entering Makkah, the armed platoon, Rasulullah ﷺ forbade.

He did not to break the treaty; outside of Makkah, these men stayed.

As had been agreed in the treaty, the Quraish had left town.

From the surrounding mountains, upon the Muslims, they looked down.

The Quraish thought, weak the Muslims had grown.

Through their worship, the Muslims' strength was shown.

The Muslims were able to visit the Ka'bah at long last.

They left Makkah, after the agreed upon three days had passed.

From on top of the mountains, the reality of Islam, the pagans did glean.

Some of the Quraish were impressed with what they had seen.

To the truth and supremacy of Islam some of them did concede.

From amongst them was the hero of Uhud, Khalid bin Waleed ﷺ.

Islam was also embraced by Uthman ibn Talhah ﷺ.

To Madinah, he was the one who escorted Umm Salamah ﷺ.

To Madinah, to accept Islam, Amr bin al-As ﷺ went.

To Abyssinia, he was one of the delegates, the Quraish had sent.

Unity ties U N I together.

The Campaign of Mu'tah

(Jumada al-Ula – 8th Year after Hijrah)

To Kill an Envoy

To the ruler of Basra, a letter Rasulullah ﷺ sent.

With the letter, al-Harith bin Umair ﷺ went.

With Caesar, the Governor of Balqa had allied.

He intercepted the letter, and had al-Harith ﷺ tied.

Governor Shurahbeel had al-Harith ﷺ beheaded.

For killing Rasulullah's ﷺ envoy, a Muslim army was readied.

The leadership of the army to Zaid ﷺ, Rasulullah ﷺ did hand.[147]

He told them if he was martyred then Ja'far ﷺ should take command.

If in the battle, Ja'far bin Abi Talib ﷺ was also to fall,

Then Abdullah bin Rawaha ﷺ was told to take control.

Rasulullah ﷺ ordered them to invite to Islam, upon reaching there,

Only If they refuse, war should they declare.

Courage and Bravery

Towards a town near Syria, three thousand Muslims set out.

Upon reaching there, the Muslims were filled with doubt.

Heraclius had mobilized an army; an army one hundred thousand strong.

The Arab tribes, which had allied with Byzantine, were also joining along.

Against such unfavourable odds, the Muslims were shaken.

The Sahabah debated about what course of action should be taken.

The army was inspired to fight, when Abdullah bin Rawaha ﷺ gave a speech,

He told them one of two, victory or martyrdom, was within their reach.

Zaid bin Haritha ﷺ fought bravely; he was fatally stabbed.

By Ja'far bin Abi Talib ﷺ, the banner was grabbed.

Ja'far's ﷺ right hand was cut off, so he transferred the banner to his left.

The left hand was cut off; he held it in his arms until, in two, he was cleft.

Abdullah bin Rawaha ﷺ took the banner and bravely fought.

He was also martyred; by the Muslims, a new leader was sought.

Khalid bin Waleed ﷺ, who had embraced Islam, was given command.

He fought against the enemy bravely; nine swords broke in his hand.

He realised the situation of the Muslims had become dire.

He thought, into the safety of the desert, the army should retire.

He reshuffled the flanks, and brought men forward from the rear.

Reinforcements had arrived, the enemy began to fear.[148]

The faces of the rear flank, to the enemy, were new.

Fear of reinforcements having arrived, in the enemy grew.

They thought, if such a small army is putting up such a good fight,

To fight fresh reinforcements, they did not possess the might.

Slowly, into the desert, the Muslim army withdrew.

The enemy thought it was a trick; they did not dare to pursue.

The enemy began retreating; they feared it was a ruse.[149]

In this battle neither did the Muslims win, nor did they lose.

Victory is not the final result, rather the manner in which you react to victory is. For a man is not praised for his defeat, he is praised for how he dealt with and overcame it.

The Conquest of Makkah

(Ramadhan – 8th Year after Hijrah)

The Broken Treaty

In the treaty of Hudaybiyah, one of the terms to which they did agree,

Was that to ally with the Muslims or the Quraish, every tribe was free.

With the Quraish of Makkah, the tribe of Banu Bakr allied,

Whilst with the Muslims, the people of Banu Khuza'ah did side.

Banu Bakr and Banu Khuza'ah were enemies from before,

To attack Banu Khuza'ah, the people of Banu Bakr did go.

With arms and men, the Quraish came to Banu Bakr's aid.

The people of Banu Khuza'ah, in an ambush, they slayed.[150]

Three options to the Quraish, Rasulullah ﷺ conveyed,

Either the blood money for Khuza'ah's victims should be paid,

Or their alliance with the Banu Bakr should be terminated,

Or for violating the terms of the treaty, it would be negated.

The Quraish gathered to discuss what they should do.

They sent Abu Sufyan to Madinah; the truce he tried to renew.[151]

In Madinah he went to his daughter, Umm Habibah's ﴿ house.

His daughter, Umm Habibah ﴿, was Rasulullah's ﷺ spouse.

He entered her house; he was about to sit.

His daughter quickly picked up the carpet.

She told him, to sit on Rasulullah's ﷺ carpet, he was unclean.

Upon hearing her words, Abu Sufyan quickly left the scene.

He went to Rasulullah ﷺ; for the renewal of the truce, he did plead.

To the renewal of the truce, Rasulullah ﷺ did not accede.

Abu Sufyan went to Abu Bakr ◌, Umar ◌ and Ali ◌, asking them to intercede.

In convincing any of them, Abu Sufyan did not succeed.

Abu Sufyan left for Makkah, in a very disappointed state.

What had happened in Madinah, to the Quraish, he did relate.

The terms of the treaty, the Quraish had breached.

For retaliation, from Rasulullah ﷺ, Banu Khuza'ah beseeched.

The Conquest

To conquer Makkah, Rasulullah ﷺ did proceed.

Ten thousand Muslims, to Makkah, he did lead.

He was joined by his uncle, Abbas ◌, on the way.

"He is the last Muhajir," Rasulullah ﷺ did say.[152]

Of the Muslim army, the people of Makkah did learn.

The Muslims intentions, Abu Sufyan went to discern.

With him Hakeem bin Hizam and Budayl bin Waraqah did go.

At Marr az-Zahran, the Muslim army they saw.

By some Muslims lookouts, these men were caught.

Into the presence of Rasulullah ﷺ, they were brought.

Finally, Abu Sufyan ◌ decided that Islam he should embrace.

He was amazed at the number of men, the Makkans were to face.

Abu Sufyan 🅰 hurried to Makkah; he told them of their plight.

He advised them, 'the Muslims they should not fight.'

'Whoever enters his house, their homes or the Masjid will not be harmed.'

The Makkans mocked Abu Sufyan 🅰; then they dispersed, alarmed.

To divide the army, Rasulullah 🅰 did decide.

From different areas, into Makkah, they would all ride.

Rasulullah 🅰 told them not to fight, except in self-defence.

In which case, the danger they should dispense.

Some ruffians of Makkah could not accept defeat.

With the battalion of Khalid bin Waleed 🅰, they did meet.

Fighting ensued between them; twelve of the pagans were killed.

After which no more blood, through fighting, was spilled.

The Humble Victor

Rasulullah 🅰 entered Makkah, riding on his camel, with his head bowed.

He was thanking Allah for the victory, and was not proud.

Today was not going to be a day of revenge and war,

Rather a day in which the sanctity of the Ka'bah, Rasulullah 🅰 would restore.

Towards the Holy Ka'bah, Rasulullah 🅰 did proceed.

To break the idols around the Ka'bah, it had been decreed.

The three hundred and sixty idols were broken, one by one.

Rasulullah 🅰 said, *"The truth has come and falsehood has gone."*

Rasulullah ﷺ asked the Quraish what they thought he was going to do.

They replied, *"We expect nothing but goodness from you."*

"I speak to you, in the same words Yusuf said to his brothers," Rasulullah ﷺ did say

He reiterated the words of Yusuf السلام, *"There is no reproach on you, this day."*

All the torture, persecution and troubles were put behind.

Only forgiveness and kindness, the Quraish did find.

The Quraish realised, in Islam, their true success lies.

They began to embrace the religion, which they once did despise.

The Ansaar of Madinah were anxious, worried and dismayed.

They feared Rasulullah ﷺ would move to the city where he once stayed.

He heard of the fear of the Ansaar, who had been there at his hour of need.

He promised that he would join them, in life and death, as had been agreed.

Revenge is a sweet poison pleasing to the soul.

Forgiveness is a bitter pill pleasing to the Lord.

The Battle of Hunayn

Strength in Numbers?

To Islam, some proud tribes were unwilling to submit.

To the conquest of Makkah, they were unable to admit.

The tribes of Hawazin, Thaqif and others combined.

To destroy Islam, a plan of war they designed.

All of their families and wealth, to the battle, these tribes brought.

They would fight bravely to ensure their safety, they thought.

The army reached Hunayn; in the valleys they were told to hide.

Hidden away, waiting for the Muslims arrival, their time they did bide.

Whilst in Makkah, of their plans, Rasulullah ﷺ came to know.

With twelve thousand men, to Hunayn, Rasulullah ﷺ did go.

Upon seeing their vast numbers, the Muslim army was appeased.

Because of their faith in numbers, Allah became displeased.

The Muslims Flee

The unaware Muslim army entered Hunayn's valley.

Suddenly, upon them, the cunning enemy did sally.

Upon the Muslim army, in great numbers arrows hailed.

The Muslim's strength in numbers had failed.

From the battlefield, many Muslims had run far away,[153]

With Rasulullah, ﷺ only a few Sahabah and kinsmen did stay.

Rasulullah ﷺ called, *"Come on people! I am the Messenger of Allah,*

I am Muhammad, the son of Abdullah."

The reins of Rasulullah's ﷺ mule, his cousin, Abu Sufyan ﷺ did hold.[154]

To return to the battle, the Sahabah, with his loud voice, Abbas ﷺ called.

When they heard Abbas ﷺ, to the battle the Muslims came.

They fought on bravely, and their honour they did reclaim.

Strength in Faith

As the battle went on, fiercer it became,

Until, the enemy, the Muslims did defame.

Defeated, the enemy fled, turning their backs,

Some Muslim battalions followed their tracks.

They left behind the wealth and families, which they had brought,

Thousands of captives, camels and sheep were caught.

To Ta'if, the majority of the defeated army had fled.

Towards Ta'if, the victorious Muslim army did head.

The Campaign of Ta'if

(Shawwal – 8 A.H.)

The City of Ta'if was a stronghold, which was well fortified.

With their leader, the enemy alliance had gone there to hide.

To break into the enemy's fort, the Muslim army tried.

But they were hailed with arrows by those who were inside.

When the Muslims neared the castle, with arrows they were hailed.

All attempts, to break into the enemy stronghold, failed.

To save his men from being attacked, Rasulullah ﷺ moved away.

For many days, around Ta'if, a siege the army did lay.

After some consultation, some suggested a frontal attack.

Others suggested they should wait for them to tire; they should stay back.

Realising swords would not work, the Muslims set up a mangonel.

Using the catapult, upon the castle, large stones the Muslims did shell.

Close to the fort, under the cover of a tank, some Muslims drew.

From on top of the fort, hot molten lead, the enemy threw.

To avoid being burnt alive, from under the cover they fled.

Now that they were in the open, many of them were shot dead.

In order to draw the enemy out of the fort,

To burning their crops, the Muslims did resort.

To stop burning their crops, the people of Ta'if pleaded.

To the enemy's request, merciful Rasulullah ﷺ acceded.

Rasulullah ﷺ told the enemy, whoever leaves the castle is free.

Some people came out; there were approximately twenty-three.

The enemy had enough supplies to last a year, Rasulullah ﷺ came to know.

Not wanting to sustain any more losses, Rasulullah ﷺ told the army to withdraw.

Fear that which is to come due to that which has gone.

Hawazin Accept Islam

Distribution of the Booty

The Muslims were unable to break in Ta'if; to their base, they retired.

Rasulullah ﷺ still needed to distribute the booty which they had acquired.

The booty was at Ji'iranah; here, for many days, Rasulullah ﷺ stayed.

Hoping that Hawazin would embrace Islam, the distribution, he delayed.

Those who had recently embraced Islam were given a larger share.

Some of the Ansaar thought this treatment was unfair.

By giving more to the new converts, towards Islam they were inclined.

But these intentions of Rasulullah ﷺ were involuntarily undermined.

The Ansaar's Share

About the Ansaar's misgivings, Rasulullah ﷺ was told,

The loyal Ansaar of Madinah were called.

Rasulullah ﷺ asked them regarding what they had disputed.

They felt it was unfair, how the booty had been distributed.

Rasulullah ﷺ said, *"Did I not come to you when you were astray,*

And through me Allah showed you the right way.

Did I not find you in a poor state?

And your needs, Allah did satiate."

Rasulullah ﷺ said "Were you not enemies, and through Allah, your hearts were unified."

"Indeed, Allah and his Rasul are better and are more gracious," the Ansaar replied.

Rasulullah ﷺ asked them, "O Ansaar! What stops you from replying to me?"

The Ansaar enquired, "O Rasulullah, what should our reply be?"

He said, "You would be saying the truth, and I would accept its truth, if you had replied,
'We accepted you, when you come to us rejected and belied.
You came to us helpless and we helped you.
When you were a fugitive, we came to your rescue.'"

"To bring these people close to the faith I wished,
The faith which you have already established.
Are you not satisfied, O Ansaar, that camels and ewes these people take,
But you go to your dwellings with the Messenger of Allah in your wake?"

The Ansaar regretted the conclusions to which they had leapt.

When they heard the touching words of Rasulullah ﷺ, they all wept.

They cried, "We are satisfied, O Rasulullah, with our lot and share."

What the Ansaar had received, to material wealth they could not compare.

Hawazin Submit to Islam

After the booty had been distributed, the Hawazin came.

The oneness of Allah, the delegation did proclaim.

For the return of their families and wealth, they did plea.

Rasulullah ﷺ asked them, which is more dear, your family or property.

The people of Hawazin replied, "Nothing, whatsoever, with kinship compares."

He told them whatever was his and Banu Abdul Muttalib's was now theirs.

The Sahabah were informed that Rasulullah ﷺ had given Hawazin his share.

Hearing this, "Whatever is ours, belongs to Rasulullah," the Sahabah did declare.[155]

To relinquish their captives the Sahabah agreed.

Like this, the captives of Hawazin were freed.

Amongst them was the daughter of Halimah 🌺.

Rasulullah 🌺 gave gifts to his foster sister, Sheyma 🌺.[156]

Fulfilling your needs will satiate you, whilst fulfilling your desires will make you hungrier.

The Expedition of Tabuk

(Rajab – 9th Year after Hijrah)

Preparation for War

Throughout the Arabian Peninsula, Islam spread like wildfire.

In the battle of Mu'tah, they had fended off the Byzantine Empire.

The strength which Islam was gaining, the Byzantines despised.

To attack the stronghold of Islam, a large force was mobilized.

To confront the enemy on their own borders, Rasulullah ﷺ did decide.

His intentions to fight the Byzantine Empire, he did not hide.

He sent messengers to tribes, telling them to prepare for war.

Into Madinah, thousands of Muslim warriors did pour.

The scorching heat of the summer desert, they would have to bear.

There were not enough camels for transport; they would have to share.

In the desert water was scarce, and food supplies were already running short.

To give as much as they could, in the path of Allah, Rasulullah ﷺ did exhort.

The Competition

When the Muslims were told that for war they should prepare,

The Sahabah brought to Rasulullah ﷺ, whatever they could spare.

With Abu Bakr ؓ, in doing good deeds, Umar ؓ used to try and compete.

He brought half of his belongings and placed them at Rasulullah's ﷺ feet

Rasulullah ﷺ asked Umar ﷺ, *"What have you left your household?"*

He had left half of what he had, Rasulullah ﷺ was told.

Umar ﷺ then waited for Abu Bakr ﷺ to arrive.

To surpass Abu Bakr ﷺ, in good deeds, Umar ﷺ did strive.

Umar ﷺ had surpassed Abu Bakr ﷺ, or so he thought.

By Abu Bakr ﷺ, from his house, everything he brought.

He placed all his belongings at Rasulullah's ﷺ feet.

Upon seeing this, Umar ﷺ finally accepted defeat.

Rasulullah ﷺ asked Abu Bakr ﷺ, *"What have you left your household?"*

"Allah and His Messenger are enough", Rasulullah ﷺ was told.

As much as they could, in Allah's path, the wealthy ones spent.

Not being able to give anything, the poor Sahabah did lament.

A Test of Faith and Courage

The Muslims were going to fight an army, which was thousands strong.

The journey across the parched desert was going to be hot and long.

For the Muslims, venturing into this expedition was a great test.

It would differentiate the ones with true faith from the rest.

The Muslim army, which set out from Madinah, was very large.

To take care of Rasulullah's ﷺ family, he left Ali ﷺ in charge.

But three Sahabah and the hypocrites stayed behind.[157]

To explain their inability to go, excuses the hypocrites did find.

On the journey, water was scarce and food was short.

To eating leaves, the Sahabah had to resort.

They took turns to ride, as transportation was less.

This is why this army was called 'the army of distress.'

When the Muslim army ran out of water,

Their precious camels, they had to slaughter.

They resorted to drinking the camel's stomach content.

Deeper and deeper, into the desert, they went.

The ruined City of Thamud, they passed,

There, they found a well at long last.

The people of the Messenger Salih ﷺ were Thamud.

With water from the well, the Sahabah prepared food.

Not to drink its water or perform ablution with it, it was later decreed.

With it the Sahabah had made dough; the dough, the camels they had to feed.[158]

Rasulullah ﷺ told the army not to enter the homes of those who did wrong.

He hurried out of the land of Thamud; not wanting to stay there for long.

Byzantine Cowers

When the Muslims reached Tabuk, the enemy they were ready to face.

But of the Byzantine army and their allies, there was no trace.

Upon hearing of the Muslim army, they had become scared.

To face the might of the Muslims, none of them dared.

With the surrounding Arab allies of Byzantine, peace was made.

With the Muslims, they agreed that tribute will be paid.

Though they returned to Madinah without having to fight,

People began to recognise Islam's true might.

Though one may turn a blind eye, it does not mean he is blind.

The Farewell Pilgrimage

(Zhu al-Hijjah – 10th Year after Hijrah)

Towards Madinah, Arab delegations raced.

By many of the tribes, Islam was embraced.

Towards the oneness of Allah, tribes were called.

Hundreds and thousands entered into Islam's fold.

To do Hajj, the fifth pillar of Islam, Rasulullah ﷺ intended.

Along with him, over a hundred thousand Sahabah attended.

Towards the end of Zhul al-Qa'dah, Rasulullah ﷺ started to prepare.

He put on his garment, applied perfume and combed his hair.

On a Saturday, four days before sighting Zhu al-Hijjah's moon,

He saddled his camel, and set off in the afternoon.

To a place called Zhu al-Hulaifah, they went.

At Zhu al-Hulaifah, the Night, they spent.

The next day, Rasulullah ﷺ wore his Ihram, and he proclaimed 'Labbayk.'

Making an intention of Hajj and Umrah, he set off with thousands in his wake.

During the days of Hajj, Rasulullah ﷺ gave many a speech,

In which the principles of Islam, to the Sahabah, he did teach.

"O people! Listen to what I say," the Sahabah, Rasulullah ﷺ did face,

"After this year, I do not know whether I will meet you at this place."

To fulfil the right of Allah and His slaves, the Sahabah he did exhort.

The sacredness of every human's blood, property and honour he taught.

"And you will be asked about me, what will you say?" an announcement he made.

The Sahabah answered, "We bear witness, the message, you have conveyed."

Towards the sky then towards the people, his blessed forefinger he did raise,

He said, "O Allah, bear witness,"; three times, he did repeat this phrase.

If there is no **unity** in h*uma***nity** then all that remains are HMA; High Maintenance Animals.

The Final Journey

(Rabi al-Awwal – 11th Year after Hijrah)

Rasulullah ﷺ Falls Ill

The responsibility of apostleship, Rasulullah ﷺ did fulfil.

Towards the end of the month of Safar, Rasulullah ﷺ fell ill.

In his illness, he would ask his wives, *"Tomorrow where shall I stay?"*

He had a fixed rota; he would live with one wife each day.

That Rasulullah ﷺ wanted to go to Aa'isha's ﷛ house, the wives understood.

To go to Aa'isha's house to stay, they told him that he could.

Aa'isha ﷛ bint Abu Bakr ﷝, was Rasulullah's ﷺ most beloved wife.

In her house, Rasulullah ﷺ spent the last days of his blessed life.

The Choice

Though our beloved Rasulullah ﷺ was barely able to walk,

A few days before his death, he went to the Masjid to talk.

To address the Sahabah, he ascended the pulpit.

Around Rasulullah ﷺ, the Sahabah did sit.

Rasulullah ﷺ told the Sahabah that Allah had given a choice, to a slave,

Between the world and the hereafter; but for the hereafter, he did crave.

"We sacrifice our fathers and mothers for you," said Abu Bakr ﷝, as he began to cry.

Abu Bakr ﷝ had realised that Rasulullah ﷺ was the slave; he had chosen to die.

In his illness, the prayer Rasulullah ﷺ still used to lead,

But now to the Masjid, he could no longer proceed.

To the Masjid, the house of Aa'isha ﷺ was joint.

To lead the prayers, Abu Bakr ﷺ he did appoint.

On Monday, by Abu Bakr ﷺ the morning prayers were being led,

When throughout the congregation much excitement spread.

Rasulullah ﷺ was stood at the entrance of Aa'isha's ﷺ door.

The Sahabah thought Rasulullah ﷺ was not ill anymore.

Abu Bakr ﷺ began to withdraw from the front, and gave way,

Thinking that Rasulullah ﷺ wanted to come out to pray.

Rasulullah ﷺ smiled at them and told them to continue.

Then back into the room of Aa'isha ﷺ he withdrew.

Last Words ...

The day before he passed away, he set all his slaves free.

He gave away any money which he had, in charity.

They had nothing left in the house that night.

Aa'isha ﷺ had to borrow oil, so that the lantern she could light.

Rasulullah ﷺ leant on Aa'isha's ﷺ shoulder, when the pangs of death started.

Saying, "O Allah, with the most exalted Companion," this world he departed.

Choosing Allah's companionship, this world he wanted to leave.

Upon the death of Rasulullah ﷺ the whole of Madinah did grieve.

إِنَّا لِلّٰهِ وَإِنَّا إِلَيْهِ رَاجِعون

'Surely we belong to Allah and to Him shall we return.'

Pause and Ponder

Reflect on some of the teachings of Rasulullah ﷺ

Alternation of the Day and Night

وَهُوَ الَّذِى جَعَلَ الَّيْلَ وَالنَّهَارَ خِلْفَةً لِّمَنْ أَرَادَ أَن يَذَّكَّرَ أَوْ أَرَادَ شُكُوراً

"And it is He (Allah) who has put the night and the day in succession, for such who desires
to remember or desires to show his gratitude."

(Surah al-Furqan – Ayah 62)

As I look up at the sky,

It reminds me of Allah, most-High.

During the day, the sun shining bright,

The moon and twinkling stars at night,

In the morning, we see first light,

It reminds me of Allah's might,

The sun, in the horizon, lifts its head,

The sky then turns a beautiful red.

Without the sun in the sky,

The earth would wilt and die.

I thank Allah for what he does give,

For giving us all blessings, to live.

Across the sky, the sun makes its way.

The sun is at its hottest at midday.

And when its journey comes to an end,

The illuminated moon, Allah does send.

The moon is a source of light,

To allow us to see in the night.

With stars, Allah decorated the sky,

Twinkling above us, so very high.

They a set path, from dusk till dawn,

The power and wisdom of Allah is shown.

Constantly, the sky overhead does change,

From red to blue, the colours range.

Next time you look up at the sky,

Remember the power of Allah most-high.

As the sky is painted, day and night,

Remember the Creator and His might.

It is the height of foolishness of the foolish one to question the wisdom of the wise.

The Wayfarer

كُنْ فِي الدُّنْيَا كَأَنَّك غَرِيبٌ أَوْ عَابِرُ سَبِيلٍ

On the authority of Abdullah ibn Umar ﷺ who said, "The Messenger of Allah ﷺ took me

by the shoulder and said, "Be in this world as though you were a stranger or a wayfarer."

(Narrated by Imam al-Bukhari ﷺ)

As I travel the journey of life,

To do good and right, I will strive.

Acknowledge this, my friend,

This road will inevitably end.

The path may look desolate and bare,

Do not despair, Allah is there.

I'm only on this road for a while,

Though it may seem too many a mile.

I may stumble, trip or even fall,

But I will never forget my goal,

To attain the pleasure of my Lord,

So why should this world I horde?

I won't follow the path on the other side.
I won't make, the devil, my road guide.
For if I listen to his lies,
It would lead me to eternal demise.

If I was to ever go astray,
It is easy to find my way.
Repentance is the path, leading back,
To get my life on the right track.

The journey looks arduous and long.
But I'll keep going steadfast and strong.
Until I reach the end of the road,
Then Paradise will be my abode.

To leave this world we have come, for we were born to die

With Difficulty Comes Ease

الصَّبْرُ عِنْدَ الصَّدْمَةِ الأُولَى

Anas ﷺ narrates that the Messenger ﷺ said, "The real patience is at the first stroke of a calamity."

(Narrated by Imam Muslim ﷺ)

Yesterday, I was flying so high.

Yesterday, I was towering in the sky.

Yesterday, I was capable of all things.

Yesterday, I was soaring without wings.

But then I realised that wings I had none,

All my hopes, dreams and ambitions now gone.

Once, with bright lights, my road shone.

Now my road is dark, am I to walk it alone?

On the road to my destination, the first step I haven't taken,

For this road to my destination seems abandoned; forsaken.

I drown in an ocean, which is made up of my worst fears.

The ocean, in which I drown, is made from my shed tears.

Everything collapsed, when I thought I had it all.

From beneath my feet, the ground did fall.

Now I'm falling, not knowing when I'm going to land.

And there is nobody present, to give me a helping hand.

They say, 'every cloud has a silver lining'; not mine,

My cloud has been shaded with a bold black line.

There's light at the end of every tunnel, they say,

But my tunnel has no end, and I've lost my way.

My friend, in the mercy of Allah, do not despair.

Wherever you look, you'll see Allah is there.

Just open your eyes, you'll be alone no more.

Allah is there; again he'll help you to soar.

They say, 'the higher you are, the harder you fall,'

Maybe you should have started with something small.

Every cloud has a silver lining? A lie you've been told,

Because, my friend, your cloud has a lining of gold.

Be assured that after every difficulty, ease will come,

Though to wait, for long, becomes difficult for some.

Be patient, for Almighty Allah's help will arrive.

In hope for reward, with patience you should strive.

You're not in a tunnel that's why it has no end.

Just raise your hands; a helping hand, Allah will lend.

Learn how to swim and don't get taken away by the tide.

And always remember; Life's a journey, treasure the ride.

Patience makes the life sweeter, for moments plucked before their time are bitter.

The Seeker of Knowledge

من يرد الله به خيرًا يفقه في الدين

Mu'awiyah ﷺ *reported: the Messenger of Allah* ﷺ *said, "When Allah wishes good for someone, He bestows upon him the understanding of Deen."*

(Narrated by Imam al-Bukhari and Imam Muslim ﷺ*)*

Out in Almighty Allah's path, I aim to learn,

Through which, the pleasure of Allah I can earn.

The banner of Islam, I will hold up high,

Until the world can see it, fluttering in the sky.

Though my efforts are nothing, my efforts are meek,

I'll keep my eyes on the road, as knowledge I seek.

Whatever I learn, I will propagate and spread,

Until I lie alone, in the stomach of the earth; dead.

From my beloved Messenger's ﷺ table spread, I do eat.

The angels spread their wings beneath my feet.

Climbing the tallest mountain, knowledge I will seek,

In the furthest of lands, even when I'm old and weak.

A seeker of knowledge, now and forever, I will be.

My goal is to be like the fruit-bearing tree,

Bowing in humility, so people can easily take.

All this I do for Almighty Allah's sake.

Asking Allah for my forgiveness, the creation does plea,

From the birds in the sky to the fish in the sea.

I am one of the inheritors of the Messengers' ﷺ wealth.

For Allah's religion, I give my money, life and health.

I will put into practice, the knowledge I gain,

Through which Paradise, I will be able to attain.

The knowledge of deen is a shining bright light,

With which my true goal in life, I can keep in sight.

Ilm (knowledge) is an everlasting candle which does not benefit unless lit with the flame of aml (acting upon it).

Selfless

رِضَا الرَّبِّ فِي رِضَا الْوَالِدِ وَسَخَطُ الرَّبِّ فِي سَخَطِ الْوَالِدِ

Abdullah bin Amr 🙵 *narrated that the Messenger* 🙵 *said: "The Lord's pleasure is in the*

parent's pleasure, and the Lord's anger is in the parent's anger."

(Narrated by Imam at-Tirmizhi 🙵*)*

One thing hard to come across is a friend who is true.

I am grateful that I am lucky enough to have two.

Two friends who would go to the end of the world, for me.

These two precious friends are priceless; not free.

You told me to be positive, when things were looking bad.

Whenever you are around, it is impossible to feel sad.

Whenever I needed someone, you were there at my side.

And if ever I had to talk to someone, in you I could confide.

I could say thank you once, and a thousand times more,

But for what you've done for me, gratitude I am unable to show.

For me, you were willing to give the whole world away.

When I needed you, you were there whether it was night or day.

A problem shared is a problem halved, or so they say.

But telling you my problem would make it all go away.

All my problems, on to your shoulders, you would take.

And you would burden yourself with it, for my sake.

Not once can I recall where you ever wore a frown.

And if I wore one you would turn it upside-down.

When I felt worthless, you made me feel worth-while.

In my heart you have left an eternal warm smile.

When I was peckish, for your extreme hunger, you did not care.

You would give me all you had, even though there was enough to share.

Your eyes filled your stomach, as you watched me happily eat.

You considered any way to help me as a delectable treat.

You would clothe me, even if you had to freeze in the cold.

You would say, "I'm boiling," and I would believe what I was told.

In the heat, you would walk by whichever side would give me shade.

When the wind blew too hard, with your body a barrier you made.

Whenever in my sleep, I groaned, moaned or sighed,

In the morning, I would wake to find you by my side.

Whenever I tossed and turned, being unable to sleep,

Worrying about what troubled me, all night you would weep.

To shower His mercy upon you, to my Lord I do call,

For all you did and how you raised me when I was small.

To grant you happiness and Paradise, to my Lord I implore.

For all my wrongdoings, Mum and Dad, your forgiveness I ask for.

Good parents give their children a head-start in life.

My parents intend to walk me to the finish line.

An Innocent Child

إِنَّ لِكُلِّ أُمَّةٍ فِتْنَةً وَفِتْنَةُ أُمَّتِي الْمَالُ

Ka'b bin 'Iyad ﷺ narrated that the Messenger ﷺ said, "Indeed there is a trial for every
Ummah, and the trial for my Ummah is wealth."
(Narrated by Imam at-Tirmizhi ﷺ)

The day I was born, when I opened my eyes,
The world around me was living a life of lies.
As I breathed my first, so I would my last.
Today I am present, tomorrow I'll be past.

From dust I was made; my return is to dust.
Death for me is unavoidable; it is a must.
But the Ummah chases the world, whilst it runs away.
And Shaytaan deceives us all, leading us astray.

The Ummah competing with one another for the world, I see,
Overlooking that death, for them, Allah surely did decree.
They hear of death and reckoning, yet they do not heed.
For the temporary world, their hearts are filled with greed.

Where the Ummah was once; where is it now?
The question I ask myself of this happening is "How?"
From such a great rise to such a disgraceful fall.
Praying for unity amongst us, to my Lord do I call.

Day and night, the Messenger ﷺ worried about us all,

Even on his deathbed, before the angel took out his soul,

Are all of the efforts, which he made, to go in vain?

Paradise is what he wanted every single Ummati to gain.

On the day when only for themselves people will care,

For us, my beloved Messenger of Allah ﷺ will be there.

When everyone will be crying "Me!" on that day,

"My Ummah, my Ummah," my Messenger ﷺ will say.

After every prayer, for his Ummah he would cry.

For our Ummah have we shed a tear from an eye?

He was the bright moon, on a dark winter's night.

The traveller's shadowy road to heaven, he did light.

So, my brothers and sisters, don't be enemies; don't fight,

Rather stand together as Muslims, and let us unite.

The way of our Messenger ﷺ, follow that straight road.

And let us prepare ourselves for our final abode.

Unity ties U N I together.

The Kindler of Peace

الظُّلْمُ ظُلُمَاتٌ يَوْمَ الْقِيَامَةِ

Abdullah Ibn Umar ﷺ narrates the Messenger ﷺ said, "Oppression will be darkness on

the Day of Resurrection."

(Narrated by Imam al-Bukhari ﷺ)

I look around at the world, and ask myself, "Why?"
Why do people live in deceit, a great lie?
I see the world I live in, and it makes my heart cry.
As I watch evil spread, all it seems I can do is sigh.

Darkness and deception is the world's shroud.
As they consume the hearts, crowd upon crowd.
Shadows from the depths of veiled souls seep.
Under the cover of a cold dark night they creep.

Around the crumbling world, oppressors roam,
Destroying; leaving no place to call home.
Wherever they go, innocent blood they spill.
The land, with rotting, dead bodies they fill.

Behind them, weeping widowed women, they leave.

In the empty streets, orphaned, crying children grieve.

Innocent civilians, as captives, they take.

They terminate everything within their wake.

Malice and hatred, in the dead hearts, do grow.

And surging in the veins of tyrants, evil does flow.

As the final flickering flame of peace quivers,

Down my spine, a sense of despair shivers.

NO! Rather, for the truth, I will stand up and rise.

To an end, I will bring these deceptions and lies.

How can I bear the blood of innocent ones being shed,

And that in cities flow rivers; rivers blood red?

How can I bear to listen to the helpless cries?

Darkness prevails, and the light of peace dies.

I will kindle the flame, and let the light spread.

So revived, are the hearts; hearts once stone dead.

The most inconsiderate one is he who put others in a position he himself would not like to be in.

The Lone Child

الْمُسْلِمُونَ كَرَجُلٍ وَاحِدٍ إِنِ اشْتَكَى عَيْنُهُ اشْتَكَى كُلُّهُ وَإِنِ اشْتَكَى رَأْسُهُ اشْتَكَى كُلُّهُ

Nu'man bin Bashir ☆ reported that the Messenger of Allah ﷺ said, "Muslims are like one body of a person; if the eye is sore, the whole body aches, and if the head aches, the whole body aches."

(Narrated by Imam Muslim ☆)

This poem is dedicated to all those innocent people whose families and homes have been torn apart by war. To all those who feel abandoned, alone, unheard, forgotten, deserted, forsaken, discarded or neglected. We're not with you but we empathise with how you feel. We're not with you but we see your sad state. We're not with you but we hear your silent cries. We're not with you but you are with us in our prayers, our thoughts and our hearts.

I look ahead of me, there's nobody there.
I look behind me, into darkness I stare.
Nor can I see anyone, when I look to my right.
And on my left, nobody is within sight.

I hear the sound of heavy footsteps fade.
In my sorrow and grief, I do wade.
Alone, on a destroyed barren land.
Deserted, the lone child, do I stand.

The land in which rivers of tears flow,
And mountains of hardship seem to grow.
Deep in the ground, seeds of discord were sown,
Due to which woods of disunity have grown.

From the sky, showers of difficulty do rain.

From the east, rose the scorching sun of pain.

Motionless in the sky, is the sun never to set?

Whether night will come to allow me to rest I fret.

At first, I could not find any aid, when I looked around.

I found the solution was to lay in prostration, on the ground.

I was only looking left and right, in front and behind.

When I turned my gaze up, the answer I did find.

Let us ensure that the rivers of tears run dry.

And that none, out of sorrow or grief, do sigh.

Let us reduce the mountains of hardship in to rubble,

So that none can be oppressed or be in trouble.

The seeds of amity and peace we will sow,

So that forests of friendship and unity will grow,

Let us chop the woods of discord down to the ground,

Making sure that, in the land, disunity is not found.

On the land, let the rains of Allah's mercy shower,

So that fruits of love, from the trees, do flower.

Let the sun of pain eternally set, far in the west,

So that the night of harmony may blanket us as we rest.

So that the lone child, I no longer remain,

Let us stand for justice, until victory we gain,

In order for peace, in the world, to prevail.

On the sea of tranquillity, let us set sail.

*If there is no **unity** in h**uma**nity then all that remains are HMA; High Maintenance Animals.*

The Stray Child

مَنْ لاَ يَرْحَمُ لاَ يُرْحَمُ

Jarir bin Abdullah 🌸 *narrates that the Messenger* 🌸 *that he said, "He who is not*

merciful (to others) will not be treated with mercy."

(Narrated by Imam Bukhari 🌸)

I stood in the shadows, into the void I stare,
At all those gushing past; does anyone care?
In my grief and agony, nobody wants to share.
Nobody shows sympathy towards how I fare.

I feel the weight of the whole world, I bear.
My already broken heart, the sorrow does tear.
A frozen look of anguish on my face I wear.
To steal a glance at me nobody does dare.

I slip onto the crowded streets; I'm cold and bear,
Shivering ,as I do not have enough clothes to wear.
Sinking in this sea of selfishness; gasping for air,
For another long and unbearable day, I start to prepare.

Famished I stagger; the road claws at my feet.
I scrounge, in the dirt, for leftovers to eat,
Unable to remember the last time I ate,
What did I do to deserve such hate?

The fervour of a warm hug, I have never felt,

Nor received a loving kiss, which made my heart melt

When has anyone ever pitied me, or even smiled?

To them, I am only a scrawny, stray, orphan child.

A loving mother or a caring father, I cannot recall.

I've been crawling on the streets since I was small.

How does it feel like to be cherished and cared for?

Deprived, of such privileges, I will never know.

I gaze through a window; a warm fire I see,

Away from their habitat, the inhabitants chase me.

The seconds of the long day creep slowly by.

As night draws in, to find a warm shelter, I try.

Despondent, I stumble through the bitter winter night,

Wondering whether I'll see tomorrow's first light.

Weak and lonely, how much longer do I have to endure?

For my wretched condition, death seems to be the only cure.

In the dead of the cruel night, in a dark alley I lie,

There's nobody to bid me farewell, as I depart and die,

I crouch in a shadowed corner; death I eagerly anticipate,

And I wonder how many more are living the same fate.

One man's kindness to another man is what makes us mankind.

What Am I?

نِعْمَتَانِ مَغْبُونٌ فِيهِمَا كَثِيرٌ مِنَ النَّاسِ، الصِّحَّةُ وَالْفَرَاغُ

Ibn `Abbas ﷺ narrates the Messenger ﷺ said, "There are two blessings which many

people lose; health and free time for doing good."

(Narrated by Imam al-Bukhari ﷺ)

I move constantly at a steady pace,

For I do not compete in anyone's race.

Even though people race against me,

I will never stop, do they not see?

When people are merry and having fun,

To them it seems with speed do I run.

And when they are grieved and feeling low,

They think that I am moving too slow.

For all I have been fixed, a limit has been set,

None can withdraw more, and fall into debt.

From your balance, not more or less will I give,

So look after and cherish me, as long as you live.

I cannot be seen, for I am in nobody's sight.

Signs of my existence are in the day and the night.

Nothing can stop me, for I cannot be caught.

I may seem long, but in reality I am very short.

I advise you, of this world make the most,

As only for a while, will I be your host.

Soon it will be that you and I will have to leave,

Let that not be a day, you mourn and grieve.

When death comes knocking on your door,

You will all wish that you had me more.

I am always moving, I wait for no one.

I am here now, soon I will be gone.

I am, in the world, the thing most sought,

But I cannot be sold, nor can I be bought.

I cannot be borrowed, nor can anyone lend.

When eternity starts, I will come to an end.

Since I have existed, people have abused me,

Not realising that I'm irreplaceable; not for free.

Not treasuring me should be considered a crime.

What am I? . . . . I am time!

Though death is inevitable, youth seems eternal.

Man's Last Thoughts

قَلْبُ الشَّيْخِ شَابٌّ عَلَى حُبِّ اثْنَتَيْنِ طُولُ الْحَيَاةِ وَكَثْرَةُ الْمَالِ

Abu Hurayrah ﷺ narrated that the Messenger ﷺ said, "The heart of an old man is young in the love for two things: long life and much wealth."

(Narrated by Imam at-Tirmizhi ﷺ)

For years, I have been trying to avoid you.

Indulged in worldly pursuits, how time flew.

Now that time has finally caught up with me,

From you, there is no place to hide or to flee.

I carried on fooling myself with the word 'tomorrow'.

If only time was a commodity, one could buy or borrow.

Tomorrow never comes, I always knew.

For a few extra moments, I'd give anything in lieu.

The day you would come had already been decreed.

You are inevitable; a visit everyone is guaranteed.

For your unanticipated arrival, I did not prepare.

I lived my life, in this mortal world, without a care.

Numerous matters unattended to, numerous things not done,

Only now I realise that this world is not all pleasure and fun.

It seems to me as though without a warning you came,

But so many people, before me, have gone through the same.

They say it's never too late to put right what's wrong,

But now that you've arrived, I realised I waited too long.

There are so many things, in this world, I'd like to amend,

But it's too late now; to these wrongs I cannot tend.

All those you visited, are now unable to tell their tale,

Each of them knew that you would arrive without fail.

Earlier than expected to many was your advent.

All of them came to this world . . . then went.

You were a thought, which occurred once in a while,

Due to which, for a few seconds, I'd be unable to smile.

Then I'd get absorbed in this world; you were gone from my mind,

Due to which of old-age and weakness, I became blind.

Regardless of who they were, you came when their time finished.

What is left of them now? To dust and bone they have diminished,

From the greatest of kings to the lowest of slaves; their lives you've taken,

Only now that I am to die, to this cruel reality do I awaken.

Fear that which is to come because of that which has gone.

Definitions

Aa

abandon	to leave or give up
abductee	a person who has been abducted or kidnapped
abhor	to hate
abide	to act according to someone's decision or rule
abjure	to reject, not to accept
absurd	to find something foolish or unreasonable
abundant	a lot, many
abuse	to cause hurt, or not treat something or someone properly
accede	to agree
accomplish	to complete, to finish something one set out to do
acknowledge	to recognize something, or to admit
acquiesce	to agree, or accept
adamant	not wanting to change your mind
address	to speak to
adore	to love
advance	to go forward
affirmative	express agreement in the positive, yes
afflict	cause pain
ahaadith	plural of hadith, a saying or act of the Messenger ﷺ.
aid	to help
al-Amin	the trustworthy one
al-Buraq	an animal which is bigger than a mule and smaller than a horse, whose step is as far as the eye can see
alcove	an indention in the wall, sometimes for seclusion
alert	to be aware
alight	to get down
alliance	to join up with another group so that both may benefit
ally	to unite with a group for both to benefit
alms	charity
amass	to gather in a large number
ambassadors	a representative of a group, country or organization

ambition	a goal which someone really wants to achieve
ambush	to attack someone by surprise
amend	to correct
ancestor	the people from whom one is descended
annihilate	to destroy
Ansaar	the people of Madinah who came to the aid of the Muslims who left Makkah
anticipate	to wait for something
anxiety	to be in a state of worry
apostate	a person who leaves their religion
appeal	to make an important request
appeased	to be happy with
approach	to come close to
arbitrate	to decide or judge between two groups
arduous	difficult and tiring
arise	to stand up, get up
array	to arrange
arrogance	pride and thinking yourself better than others
artery	a tube through which blood flows
ascend	to climb up
ascertain	to find out the truth regarding a matter
ascribe	to attribute or credit someone with something
Asr	the prayer which is read late in the afternoon
assassination	to kill an important person secretly
assign	to give someone a job to do
assist	to help with something
assuage	to satisfy
assure	to make sure
astray	to go off the right path
at-tahiyyat	is the conversation which Rasulullah ﷺ had with Allah when they first met in Mi'raaj
attempt	to try
attest	to bear witness
attire	clothing
attitude	the way a person behaves, feels or thinks

authority	someone in the position of power
avenge	to take revenge
aware	to know and recognise something

Bb

bade	to bid someone a greeting or farewell, past tense of bid. It also means to tell someone to do something
bald	to have no hair
banish	to force someone to leave a place
bar	to stop
bare	uncovered, not having anything
barren	unable to have a child, or land which is unable to grow vegetation
battalion	a group of people ready for battle
bawl	to scream or cry
Bay'at e-Ridwan	literally the 'pledge of happiness', this is the pledge taken at Hudaybiyah under the tree with which Allah was very pleased
Bayt ul-Ma'mur	the building directly above the Ka'bah in the seventh heaven which 70000 angels circumambulate everyday
bear	to tolerate
Bedouins	nomadic tribes, people who live in the desert and move around in search of water and vegetation
befit	to be appropriate
begrudge	to unhappily accept
belied	to be falsified
belief	to accept something as true, a firm conviction in the truth of a statement
beseech	to ask, to plead
bestow	to grant, give
betray	to hand over something of trust to someone's enemy who considered you to be a friend
bide	to stay somewhere
blessing	a favour
blood money	the money owed for someone's murder
blunder	mistake

booty	the spoils of war, goods left on the battlefield
bore	to give birth
boycott	a ban which forbids communication, transactions or relations with a group
breach	to break a contract or law
brute	animal like, very strong
burden	a heavy load

Cc

capable	to be able to do something
caravan	olden times; the group of people who used to travel with camels and horses loaded with goods
cease	stop
Caesar	the ruler of the Byzantine Empire
celestial	heavenly
chaste	to be pure
cherish	to love
chieftain	leader
Choroes	the leader of the Persian Empire
civil war	a war which happens between two groups of people from the same place
clan	a large extended family
clause	a condition in a treaty
cleft	to split, divide
clemency	mercy, to be kind
clergy	people given religious duties
companion	a friend, one with whom someone spends time with
commence	to start
commodity	goods, valuable thing
comply	to do something according to how someone wishes
conceive	to come up with a plan, to be with child
conclude	to bring to an end
condemn	to disapprove of something harshly
confederates	groups which have joined up
confer	to give, to have a discussion with
confess	to admit

confide	to tell someone something in private and trust them not to tell anyone
confront	to meet face to face, to face up to something
congregation	gathering
conquest	to come into control of an a place with an army
contribute	to take part, to give towards a cause
consent	to give permission
conspire	to make a plan to harm someone
consult	to discuss with someone
consume	to eat
contemplation	to think deeply
content	what something consists of, when one feels at peace they are said to be content
contract	an agreement
contradict	to speak the opposite of what someone else said
contrive	to come up with
convene	to call together
convert	to change, to leave one religion or idea for another
convey	to pass on something to someone, to get something across to someone
conviction	a firm belief,
convince	to cause someone to believe something
cope	to bear with
cower	to be scared
crave	to strongly desire something, to want
crucify	to hang or nail someone on a cross
current	the direction in which the water flows, also means now
customary	as is usual in a given situation

Dd

daily	everyday
Dar un-Nadwa	the house in which matters of Makkah used to be decided
dawn	the first light of day
debate	to argue
debt	money which is owed
deceive	to make someone believe something which is not true

decrease	to become less
decree	to order given by someone in power
dedicate	to commit oneself to something
deed	an action
deen	religion
defame	to make someone look bad
defecate	to excrete stool,
delay	to make late
delegation	a group which come or goes as a representative
demise	death
denounce	inform against something,
deplete	to use up, gradually finish
descend	to come down
descendant	to be the child of
deserted	to leave a place empty
desire	to want
desolate	to be empty
despair	to lose hope
despondent	to be sad having lost hope
destination	place where one wants to go
determination	to be firm in an outcome one wants to achieve
devise	to come up with
devote	to be loyal, give oneself to something
devout	to give oneself to a cause or religion
deity	god
differentiate	to be able to tell the difference
diminish	to gradually decrease
dine	to eat
dire	a very serious situation
disbeliever	one who does not believe (is not a Muslim)
discard	to throw away
discern	to recognize
disclose	make something known
discord	disagreement between people

disfigure	to spoil something's appearance
disgrace	to lose respect, bring shame
dishearten	to lose heart, lose hope
dismay	to be in distress, to be saddened
dismiss	to order someone to leave
dismount	to get of an animal
dispatch	to send off
dispense	to distribute or supply, to get rid of
disperse	to go in different directions
dispute	disagreement
dissension	disagreement which leads to a quarrel
dissuade	to convince someone not to do something
distress	to be extremely worried or in pain
divert	to cause something or someone to change course
divine	from Allah
doubt	to be unsure
draw a lot	to take a random pick from a selection
dread	not looking forward to
drought	a shortage of water
due	something which needs to be given is said to be due

Ee

eager	to want to do something
eloquent	speech which is clear and persuasive
emigration	to leave ones hometown for another place
emotion	a feeling
emphasize	to give greater importance to something
encompass	to include all areas, surround
encounter	to come across
endure	to put up with
enlist	to get the support of someone for a cause
enquire	to ask
ensure	to make sure
entrails	the guts, internal body parts of an animal
environment	the surrounding

envoy	a messenger who had been sent to deliver a message
equality	being equal, fair and just
era	a time-span
establish	to set up permanently
eternal	lasting forever
evacuate	to leave
exchange	to give one thing for another
exert	to try hard
exhort	to urge someone to do to something
exile	being forbidden to return to a one's hometown
expectorate	to spit
expedition	a journey taken by a group
expelled	to force one to leave a place
expose	to show something up
express	to convey ones thoughts

Ff

faithful	loyal
famine	shortage of food
famish	to be extremely hungry
fast	known in Arabic as sawm. Not to eat, drink or engage in relations with one's spouse from dawn till sunset.
feat	an achievement which requires an effort
felled	to be knocked down
fend off	to fight off, or prevent
fervour	to be emotionally excited
flaw	fault, mistake
flock	a group of animals, the gathering of many people
foe	enemy
forefathers	an ancestor
forgiveness	to let go of an offence someone caused you
forsake	to leave
fortify	to make something strong
foundation	the base or ideal upon which everything else is built
fragrance	good smell

frequent	often
fugitive	a person who has escaped and is in hiding
furious	angry
futile	useless or pointless

Gg

garrison	soldiers who are placed to defend from outside attacks
gratitude	to be thankful
guarantee	to assure or promise
guardian	one who looks after, protector
guide	one who shows the way

Hh

harass	to abuse
hardship	difficulty
harmony	to live peacefully or work peacefully
harsh	severe
haste	hurry, to do an action very quickly
hatch	to come up with a plan
hath	old English for 'has'
heed	to take notice of
heir	one who inherits after a person passes away
hesitate	to be wary of doing something
hire	to borrow or employ someone for money
honour	a lot of respect and esteem
horde	a large group of people, to accumulate in great amounts
hospitality	to look after ones friends, family or stranger at one's home
host	the one who looks after the guests needs
hostage	a person who is kept as a guarantee for a condition
hostile	unfriendly
humanity	the human race
humble	to deem oneself as low
humiliation	to be disgraced
humility	humbleness, *see humble*

Ii

ihram	to enter into the state when things which were previously

	allowed become forbidden, the two pieces of cloth worn when one intends to go for holy pilgrimage
illuminate	light up
imaan	faith
impending	coming up soon
implore	to ask pleadingly
incident	something which has happened
incite	to stir up, persuade
incline	side towards something
increase	to become more
indicate	to point towards
indulge	to be engrossed in something
inevitable	something which is definite to occur
infidelity	to be unfaithful
infiltrate	to break into by stealth
infuriate	to make angry
inhabitant	one who lives in a place is said to be its inhabitant
inherit	to acquire something on the death of someone
initially	at the beginning
Injeel	Arabic for the Gospel, the New Testament
innocent	to be free of fault, not guilty
insist	to demand, to not take no for an answer
instil	to introduce something slowly
insult	to cause offence
intend	what one plans to do
intercept	to be an obstruction in the passage of something or someone
intercession	to try and influence someone's decision on behalf of someone else
intervene	to come in-between to try and change the outcome
invent	to come up with, to make up
invoke	call upon

Jj

Jamada al-Ula	fifth month of the Islamic Calendar
janazah salaah	the funeral prayer

Jibra'eel ﷺ	the Archangel, who used to bring messages of Allah to the messengers
jihad	holy war
join ties	to strengthen relationships

Kk

kin	family and relatives
kindred	family and relatives
kith	friends

Ll

lag	to trail behind
lament	to mourn and grieve over something
lantern	a lamp
lean	thin
leniency	to show kindness in one's treatment even though they deserve something more severe
lieu	in exchange
livid	extremely angry
loin	the private area

Mm

maintain	to keep up
malice	hatred, wanting to do something evil
mangonel	catapult
manoeuvre	a planned movement created in order to achieve something
manuscript	a book or document
martyr	one who has been killed in special cause, usually religious
measly	small or few
measure	A unit which allows one to determine the height, mass length of an object, or action, or bowl with which one measures
meek	humble
merciless	without mercy, unkind
merry	happy
migration	to leave one place for another
miracle	a divine action which humans are not capable of doing
mobilize	to get ready, usually an army

mock	to make fun of something
mourn	to grieve, be sad at the loss of something
Muhaajir	those Muslims who left Makkah for Madinah in order to be able to practice their religion freely
Muharram	first month of the Islamic year
muse	to think over
mushrik	polytheist, one who believes in more than one god
muted	to be silenced
mutilate	to disfigure

Nn

nation	a large group of people who have a common country, ancestor or history
negate	to stop something being effective
negotiate	to try to reach an agreement over a dispute by discussing
Negus	the King of Abyssinia
norm	that which is normal

Oo

oath	a promise
obligation	something which a person feels they have to do
odds	chances
onslaught	a fierce attack
opportunity	a chance
oppose	to go against
oppress	to treat someone unfairly
orphan	a child whose father passes away before he reaches maturity
outrage	anger
outskirt	on the outside of a town
overrated	to give something more credit than it deserves

Pp

pact	an agreement between two groups
pangs	sharp pains
parley	to talk, speak
partake	to take part of
passage	a way through

patience	not getting angry or upset during suffering
peak	at the top of
perceive	to realize
perish	to be destroyed
permit	to allow
persecution	to treat someone badly because of their belief, race gender etc.
persevere	to stay steadfast and strong on a course of action
persistence	not giving up
persuade	to convince someone by pointing out benefits
pursue	to go after
pilgrim	one who is on a holy journey
pity	to feel sorry for someone
platoon	a part of an army which has been separated from the main army for a tactical reason
plead	to ask imploringly
pledge	a promise
plight	a dangerous situation
plot	plan, a piece of land
plunder	to take goods at the time of war
ponder	to think about
portion	a piece of something
possess	to have as one's own, to take in control
preach	to teach publicly
precautionary-measure	an action done in case to prevent something which could happen
precedence	to give preference over, to regard as more important
prefer	to like something more than something else
pre-Islamic	before Islam
prevent	to put a stop to something
pride	to be pleased with oneself
proceed	to go forward
proclaim	announce publicly
procure	to get something
proffer	to offer

proficient	to be very good at something
profit	a monetary gain
propagate	to spread
proposal	an offer put forwards, also used for when one asks someone for their hand in marriage
proposition	a proposal
prostration	to bow on the floor with the head, feet, hands and knees touching the ground
protection	to look after someone making sure they are not harmed
provision	food
pulpit	a raised platform from which one delivers a speech

Qq

quarters	place where one stays
quell	to put to an end
quench	to put an end to ones thirst

Rr

Rabbi	a Jewish priest
Rabi ul-Awwal	Third month of the Islamic calendar
Rajab	seventh month of the Islamic Calendar
rally	come together in order to fight
ram	a male sheep
Ramadhan	ninth month of the Islamic calendar
ransom	money paid for the release of a prisoner
rebuke	to tell of by showing ones disapproval
recall	to remember
reclaim	to come back into the possession of something
recompense	to pay back for something one has done wrong
reconstruct	to rebuild
redeem	to recover
reduce	to become less
reflect	ponder, think over
refrain	to stay away from
refuge	to be in the state of safety from danger
refugee	a person forced to leave their home town or country due to persecution, violence or a disaster

reiterate	to repeat
reject	to turn something down
relate	narrate, to tell a story or incident
relief	aid, to find comfort from pain
relinquish	to give over
reluctant	to hesitate, unwilling to do something but feel obliged to do so
remain	to stay
renegade	one who leaves their religion or country and places allegiance elsewhere
repent	to express sorrow for past actions
reproach	to show disapproval of past actions
request	to ask
resemble	to look like
resentment	to feel bad at what one considers as unfair treatment
reside	to live
resign	to give up
resist	stand against
resolve	to find a solution to a problem
resort	to turn to a certain action to solve a problem
resurrect	to bring back to life after death
retaliate	to return an attack or insult after being attacked or insulted
retort	to reply harshly
retreat	to fall back
retribution	a punishment given which one feels the punished deserves
revoke	put an end to something
rota	a schedule for things one has to do at certain times
roused	awaken
ruffian	violent person
rumour	gossip spread from person to person
ruse	a trick

Ss

Sabbath	for Jews the Saturday on which they are not allowed to work

sacred black stone	in Arabic 'al-hajr al-aswad.' A stone from heaven which is placed at one corner of the Ka'bah.
sacrifice	slaughtering an animal for Allah or to give ones possessions away to please Allah
saalah	prayer
Safar	second month of the Islamic calendar
sally	to suddenly rush out and attack
sanctity	being holy
satiate	to satisfy
scarce	rare, not readily available
scheme	a devised plot
scold	to harshly tell someone off
scorching	extremely hot
scrawny	small, thin, bony
scripture	sacred writing
scrounge	to look for
seclude	to go into privacy
seek	to look for
sense	felt
septic	infected
sever	to cut off
severe	very great
Sha'ban	Eighth month of the Islamic calendar
Shawwal	tenth month of the Islamic calendar
sheathed	something which is in a sheath, a covering which protects it
Sidrat ul-Muntaha	a large tree at the furthest limit which cannot be crossed except with the permission of Allah
siege	to surround a place one cannot break into in order to try and get them to surrender when supplies run out
sincere	being true in ones actions, not doing an action with pretence deceiving the onlooker
site	place
slay	to kill
smite	to hit
solution	answer

sought	looked for
spied	*see sneakily*
spouse	husband or wife
spurn	to turn away, reject
station	guards,
steer	to direct
stem	stem the flow of, to confine, try to stop
stern	serious
subdue	bring under control
submit	to give into something
subservience	to comply to the wishes of another
successor	an heir, inheritor, one who takes the position of someone after their death
summon	to call forward
supplication	a prayer
support	to help, give ones assistance to
supremacy	power and authority
suspend	hang
sympathy	to feel sorry for

Tt

tactics	a plan or strategy made to achieve ones goals
taunt	something said in order make someone angry
tend	care for
testify	to declare something to be the truth
threat	for one to say they intend to cause harm to another
throng	to rush towards, for a large group to gather in a small place
thus	as a result
tidings	news (generally good news)
tolerate	to put up with
torment	to cause pain
trace	sign, mark, trail
trade	to exchange one thing for another
tranquillity	peace, to be at ease
transpire	to occur, to happen

treacherous	being deceitful, betraying
trial	a test, a gathering kept to decide whether someone is innocent or guilty
tribe	large extended family, clan
tribulation	a test which causes suffering
trust	to believe someone to be true and reliable
tyrant	a cruel ruler

Uu

Umrah	the lesser pilgrimage, in which one circles around the Ka'bah seven times, walks between the two mountains of Safa and Marwa seven times and shaves one's head
unanimously	when everyone agrees
unchaste	impure, disloyal
undefended	can be easily attacked
unfavourable	not in ones favour, when the odds are against someone
unite	to get together for a common purpose
unity	being united, living together without any fighting
uphold	maintain, support
upper-hand	being in a better position, having an advantage
uprising	a rebellion

Vv

vain	for one to feel greatly important, thinking greatly of one's self
valour	the quality of a hero
various	many different types
vegetation	plants and trees
verdict	a decision
vice	evil, sin
vigour	with a lot of energy
vindicate	prove someone's innocence, show something to be right or true
violate	to go against the terms of an agreement
vulnerable	someone who can easily be attacked physically or emotionally

Ww

wake	to go along with

waver	to be unsteady
weary	tired
welfare	health and happiness of someone
welled	to have strong emotions for something
wilderness	in the wild
will	the document which states how ones possessions should be distributed after their death
willingness	to happily do something
withdrew	to take out or fall back
withhold	to hold back
wittingly	cleverly, slyly
wrath	extremely angry
wretched	very bad

Yy

Zz

zeal	eager, enthusiastic
Zhu al-Hijjah	Twelfth month of the Islamic calendar
Zhu al-Qa'dah	eleventh month of the Islamic calendar

Endnotes

Arabia Before Rasulullah's ﷺ Birth

[1] Some people considered the birth of a girl in their home as a great shame. Whilst some felt that their daughters would not be able to earn for them and they would be unable to provide for them. For these reasons they would kill their own daughters.

The Year of the Elephant

[2] It has been narrated that an Arab who visited Yemen saw the church which had been built to compete with the Ka'bah. The Arab defecated by the church which infuriated Abrahah. Abrahah resolved to break the Ka'bah due to this insult.

[3] When the birds struck them with stones of hard clay the army became like eaten straw.

From Birth to Marriage

[4] Rabi ul-Awwal is the third month of the Islamic calendar. There are various views regarding the exact date of his birth.

[5] The donkey was the same but the rider was different, now the blessed Messenger of Allah ﷺ rode on that donkey.

[6] They would not produce any milk.

[7] His grandfather was Abdul Muttalib.

[8] Sham was a large area consisting of many of today's countries. It is usually translated as Syria, however it also included areas of its surrounding countries.

[9] People used to call him al-Amin which means 'the trustworthy one'.

[10] When Khadijah ؓ heard of the qualities and noble characteristics of Rasulullah ﷺ from her slave Maysarah, she was impressed and thus made known her desire to marry Rasulullah ﷺ.

From Marriage to Apostleship

[11] The punishment that befell the 'people of the elephant' was still fresh in the minds of the people. They were afraid that Allah would punish them for trying to break down the Ka'bah. Finally al-Waleed bin Mughirah al-Mukhzumi started the work. When people saw that no harm came to him the others participated in demolishing the walls until they reached the foundation.

¹² Allah protected Rasulullah ﷺ from exposing himself again. It is also said that this incident occurred when Rasulullah ﷺ was a child.

¹³ In Arabic the Black Stone is known as Hajar ul-Aswad. This stone was sent down from heaven by Allah. It is sunnah to kiss the Black Stone. Whosoever kisses it, all their sins are forgiven. It was previously white in colour but due the sins of man it gradually became black.

¹⁴ It was Abu Umayyah bin Mughirah al-Makhzumi, one of the oldest from amongst the chiefs that suggested this.

¹⁵ This is how Rasulullah ﷺ averted a civil war. Each clan felt as though they had been given the honour of placing the stone in its place.

¹⁶ His daughters were; Zainab ﵂, Umm Kulthum ﵂, Ruqayya ﵂ and Fatimah ﵂.

¹⁷ People began to call him Zaid ibn Muhammad ﷺ. However after prophethood when Allah revealed, "O you believers, call the adoptive sons with their actual parentage," he was then referred to by his father's name, Zaid bin Haritha ﵃.

¹⁸ A cave approximately two miles from Makkah on the 'Mountain of Light' (Jabal Nur).

The First Revelation

¹⁹ In preparation for revelation Allah made it such that whatever Rasulullah ﷺ dreamt at night he would see it happening in the morning.

²⁰ Surah al-Alaq, Verses 1-5.

²¹ Waraqah bin Nawfal was a monotheist and had studied the previous scriptures. Upon hearing the ordeal of Rasulullah ﷺ he realised that he was the last Messenger whose tidings had been foretold in the scriptures.

²² Waraqah ﵃ knew from the previous scriptures that Rasulullah ﷺ would be driven out of Makkah.

²³ Surah Mudath'thir is the 74th chapter of the Qur'an.

Preaching Begins

²⁴ *See introduction for explanation.*

Persecution

²⁵ The fat melting from his back would put out the coals.

[26] Summayyah ﷺ was the first person to be martyred for the cause of Islam. Abu Jahl drove a spear through her.

[27] Abu Bakr ﷺ freed many Muslim slaves, one of them was Bilal ﷺ.

The Migration to Abyssinia

[28] The king was a Christian. The two ambassadors tried to incite him against the Muslims by telling him that they were neither Christian nor polytheists.

[29] They ate dead animals, ones that had died naturally and had not been slaughtered.

[30] Surah Maryam is the 19th chapter of the Qur'an.

[31] The King realised that the words from the Qur'an were from the same Being that had revealed the Injeel (Gospel).

[32] The two men again tried to incite hatred towards the Muslims by telling the king that their beliefs regarding Isa ﷺ did not conform to that of the Christians. Whilst the Christians said Isa ﷺ was the son of god, Muslims maintained that he was a servant and messenger of Allah.

[33] The King followed original Christianity and thus believed that Isa ﷺ was not the son of God. Thus the plan of the Quraishi dignitaries failed.

[34] News reached the Muslims in Abyssinia that the people of Makkah had come to an agreement with the Muslims and that they were living in harmony. Longing to go home and desiring a reunion with the Muslims and their families they returned to Makkah. However when they reached Makkah they found that the persecution was more severe than before. This time more Muslims migrated to seek refuge in Abyssinia.

Hamzah ﷺ Accepts Islam

[35] Hamzah ﷺ was infuriated that his nephew had been harassed. Though he had not yet accepted Islam he was unable to tolerate his nephew being hurt.

[36] It was after this that Hamzah ﷺ decided to come into the fold of Islam.

Umar ﷺ Accepts Islam

[37] In some books it is mentioned that it was Nu'aym bin Abdullah ﷺ who met Umar ﷺ on the way.

[38] Sa'd ﷺ wanted to divert Umar's ﷺ attention so that he could warn Rasulullah ﷺ of Umar's ﷺ intention to kill him.

The Boycott

39 Some Makkans convened to bring an end to the boycott. To make it seem as though many of them were against the pact one by one they went to Abu Jahl and told him that they disagreed with the pact and disagreed with what they were doing with their own kith and kin. But Abu Jahl realised that they had planned all this before and dismissed their objections.

40 Rasulullah ﷺ had been informed by Allah that the pact had been eaten up by white ants.

41 They saw that what Rasulullah ﷺ had said with regards to the ants having eaten the words of the pact was true. As promised they had to bring an end to the pact. Observe how Abu Talib was ready to make his whole tribe bear hardships and difficulty but was not willing to hand Rasulullah ﷺ over to them. He loved his nephew to such an extent that he would make his location unknown at night so that nobody could assassinate him. But why does he willingly say he will hand his nephew over to them if the information regarding the ants having eaten the pact was untrue? This was because of his infallible belief in the words of his nephew. Even though he had not accepted Islam he knew his nephew's words were true and he was thus willing to gamble his nephew's life on them. Now reflect on our lives. We have accepted Islam, so should our faith in Rasulullah's ﷺ words not be stronger than that of a disbeliever?

The Year of Grief

42 It has been narrated that the injuries were so severe that the blood flowing from his body caused his feet to stick to his sandals. Aa'isha ﷺ once asked Rasulullah ﷺ if he had experienced a day more severe than the day of the battle of Uhud. Rasulullah ﷺ then mentioned to her this incident that befell him in Ta'if.

43 This incident sheds light on the compassion that Rasulullah ﷺ had for each and every single individual. He did not want the people destroyed, hoping that one of their progeny might worship Allah alone and not associate any partners with Him. Despite this day being the most severe on Rasulullah ﷺ he did not return unto his nation except patience, forbearance and good will.

The Night Journey – al-Isra

44 Umm Hani ﷺ was the daughter of Abu Talib, therefore she was the cousin of Rasulullah ﷺ.

45 Al-Buraq is a steed which is smaller than a mule but bigger than a donkey.

The animals step is so wide that it reaches the farthest point within the reach of the animal's sight.

[46] Azhaan and iqaamat are the call to prayers.

[47] All the messengers had gathered at Masjid ul-Aqsa. Rasulullah ﷺ led them in prayer which signified him being the leader of all messengers.

The Ascension – Al-Mi'raaj

[48] There are guardians at each of the seven heavens that only permit those to pass who have been called by Allah.

[49] At each heaven the guardian would ask who they were and whether they had been called.

[50] For description of Bayt ul-Ma'mur see definitions

[51] For description of Sidrat ul-Muntaha see definitions.

[52] Initially Allah gifted Rasulullah ﷺ with fifty prayers that were made incumbent upon the Ummah. When Moosa ﷺ was told that fifty prayers had been enjoined upon the Ummah he recollected the hardships that Banu Isra'eel put him through. He felt that the whole Ummah would not be able to fulfil the obligation, so he advised Rasulullah ﷺ to go and get them reduced. When Rasulullah ﷺ went back they were reduced by five. Moosa ﷺ felt forty five was also too much for the Ummah to cope with. So Rasulullah ﷺ went again and they were again reduced by five again. This continued occurring until the total had reached five. Moosa ﷺ felt five was too much also but this time Rasulullah ﷺ felt embarrassed to go and ask for a reduction.

[53] It has been said that it was after this incident that Abu Bakr ﷺ received the title of as-Siddeeq, due to his unwavering faith in Rasulullah ﷺ.

The Pledge

[54] Prior to accepting Islam, Mus'ab bin Umair ﷺ was the best dressed youth in Makkah. His parents spent lavishly on him and he lived a luxurious life but they were greatly displeased when he accepted Islam. He sacrificed all his comforts and was now living in poverty and squalor.

[55] The people of Madinah wanted Rasulullah ﷺ to join them in their city and preach the true religion from Madinah.

The Hijrah – Migration to Madinah

[56] The Muslims had started to migrate to Madinah in small groups.

57 Abu Salamah 🕮 passed away from a wound he sustained during the battle of Uhud. The Muslims felt they had a duty towards Umm Salamah 🕮 who had no family in Madinah. She had young children to take care of, so Abu Bakr 🕮 sent a proposal to her, which she declined. Then Umar 🕮 sent a proposal to her which she too declined. When Rasulullah 🕮 proposed to her she gladly accepted and was thus married to Rasulullah 🕮 and became one of the 'Mothers of the believers'.

58 Uthman bin Talhah had not yet embraced Islam. He accepted Islam in the seventh year after the Hijrah.

59 Abu Jahl is known as the 'Firown of this Ummah'. It is said that his vanity and pride surpassed that of Firown. After the battle of Badr Rasulullah 🕮 sent the Sahabah to see if they could locate Abu Jahl amongst the dead. Abdullah ibn Masood 🕮 found him in the throes of death. Abu Jahl was severely wounded and was unable to move. Abdullah ibn Masood 🕮 climbed onto his chest. Even in this moment of helplessness rather than bringing imaan or pleading for mercy he said to Abdullah ibn Masood 🕮, "O Shepherd, you have stood upon a very strong mount." He then asked Abdullah ibn Masood 🕮, "For whom was the victory?"
Abdullah ibn Masood 🕮 replied, "For Allah and his Rasul." Then Abu Jahl requested Abdullah ibn Masood 🕮 that when you sever my head then cut it from as close to the chest as possible, so that when it is put amongst the other severed heads it towers over them. In life he was proud, in death he showed pride and even after death he wanted to show pride. Whereas when Firown saw his imminent death he cried out that he believed in the god in which Banu Isra'eel believed, though it was too late.

60 Just as the nation of Thamud had planned to assassinate Salih 🕮, similarly the pagans made a plan. They too decided to have many youths attack at once so that the person who delivered the fatal blow would be unknown. They therefore felt that retribution against one specific clan would not be possible and Rasulullah's 🕮 family would not be able to fight against all the tribes that were involved.

61 Rasulullah 🕮 was known for his honesty and trustworthiness. Despite not accepting him as a Messenger of Allah 🕮 the disbelievers would still give him their prized and valuable possessions for safekeeping. These same people had now gathered to assassinate him, yet Rasulullah's 🕮 sublime character drove him to ensure that their valuables were safely returned to them. He told Ali 🕮 to make sure he returns all the things that were given to him as a trust before Ali 🕮 migrates to Madinah.

^{62} In spite of knowing that the enemy could burst in and attack the one sleeping in the bed, Ali fell asleep. Ponder over the faith they had in Allah and his Messenger that it allowed him to fall asleep.

^{63} Rasulullah headed south even though Madinah was north. The enemy knew Rasulullah intended to go to Madinah so they would try and pursue him on the road to Madinah.

^{64} The insect continued stinging Abu Bakr but he would not move as Rasulullah had rested his head on his lap. He did not want to cause Rasulullah the slightest inconvenience by waking him up, so he did not move. Unbidden tears came to his eyes and he was unable to them stop from falling on Rasulullah's noble face. The tear drop woke Rasulullah up and when he realised what had happened he applied his blessed saliva on the wound which cured it.

^{65} Abdullah was the son of Abu Bakr.

^{66} Rasulullah comforted him saying that Allah was with them and Allah would protect them.

^{67} Despite the closeness of their companionship, Rasulullah insisted that he pays for the camel. Every act of Rasulullah is a blessing for the Ummah from which we can learn a lesson.

^{68} His name was Suraqah bin Malik. He had been informed of three riders travelling away from Makkah. He slipped out of Makkah unseen and rushed towards the place where they had been seen in order to claim the reward for the capture of Rasulullah and Abu Bakr.

^{69} When a situation befell anyone they would draw lots to choose which course of action to take. So Suraqah drew lots to ascertain whether or not he should continue giving chase. The lot that was drawn stated he should withdraw but he was blinded by greed and went against the lot.

^{70} He had reached quite close to Rasulullah and called out to him asking for forgiveness.

^{71} Rasulullah first put Islam forward to Suraqah which he refused. So Rasulullah asked him to divert people away from him.

^{72} Abu Ma'bad was shocked that goats which he had taken to graze did not produce any milk whereas the goat that was left at home and had not grazed in any pastures had given milk.

^{73} Again Abu Bakr does not pay attention to his exhaustion. He knew that

Rasulullah ﷺ was tired from his long journey so he presented himself to the people. The people of Madinah had not seen Rasulullah ﷺ so they assumed that Abu Bakr ؓ was the Messenger and they gathered around him whilst Rasulullah ﷺ rested. When rays from the sun fell on Rasulullah ﷺ, Abu Bakr ؓ could not bear to see him experience even the slightest discomfort so he went to shade him from the heat. Only then were the people able to distinguish who Rasulullah ﷺ was. This incident also points towards the humility and simplicity of Rasulullah ﷺ. He did not arrive in pomp and grandeur, he lived amongst the people such that one could not tell who the leader amongst them was.

74 Madinah was originally called Yathrib. After the arrival of Rasulullah ﷺ it became known as Madinat un-Nabi ﷺ, which means 'the City of the Messenger ﷺ'.

75 Shu'ayb ؓ sacrificed all his wealth to be allowed to travel to Madinah in peace. Rasulullah ﷺ had been informed from the heavens of the deal Shu'ayb ؓ had made. As soon as Shu'ayb ؓ arrived and came upon Rasulullah ﷺ he was told, 'Fruitful was your trade'. His exchanging of wealth for migration was an excellent transaction, the reward of which will be seen in the hereafter.

In Madinah

76 Muhajireen were those who had emigrated from Makkah to Madinah to safeguard their faith. The Ansaar were the people of Madinah who assisted those who had emigrated from Makkah.

77 They were the tribes of Qurayzah, Qaynuqa and Nadeer.

78 As the questions were such that only a messenger would have knowledge of them, Abdullah bin Salam ؓ attested to the apostleship of Rasulullah ﷺ and embraced Islam.

79 Abdullah bin Salam ؓ informed Rasulullah ﷺ that if the people hear about his conversion to Islam they will degrade him. So Rasulullah ﷺ called them and asked them with regards to Abdullah bin Salam ؓ. The Jews praised him highly. When Abdullah bin Salam ؓ came in front of the Jews and they were told of his conversion they began calling him the worst amongst them.

80 The hypocrites were those who claimed to have accepted Islam but in reality they harboured enmity for Islam and would plan ways in which they could cause discord amongst the Muslims.

[81] Bark al-Ghimad is said to be a very far place in Yemen or a place in Abyssinia.

[82] The Ansaar had pledged that they would defend Rasulullah ﷺ in Madinah. Now they were out of Madinah they had no obligation to fight. The Muhajireen had made known their willingness to fight however the Ansaar out of respect had not spoken. Sa'd bin Mu'adh ؓ realised Rasulullah ﷺ wanted to know where the Ansaar stood with regards to the possible forthcoming battle.

[83] Rasulullah ﷺ entreated Allah that if they were defeated then none would be left to continue the effort, as the deen of Allah had not yet been completely established.

[84] At the beginning of a battle it was customary for courageous warriors from each side to ride out and issue a challenge. When there was nobody left to make or accept a challenge the general battle would ensue. Three men rode out from the ranks of the pagans, they were Utbah bin Rabi'ah, Shaybah bin Rabi'ah and Walid bin Utbah. Three men from the Ansaar came forth to accept the challenge. They were Abdullah ibn Rawaha ؓ, Auf ibn Afra ؓ and Muawwidh ibn Afra ؓ. When the three pagans saw that they were not from the Quraish, they refused to fight them saying their conflict was not with them.

[85] Rasulullah ﷺ sent out his uncle Hamzah ibn Abdul Muttalib ؓ, his cousins Ali ibn Abi Talib ؓ and Ubaydah ibn al-Harith ibn Abdul Muttalib ؓ. Ali ؓ and Hamzah ؓ finished off their opponents however Ubaydah ؓ was injured. So the two of them went to Ubaydah's ؓ assistance and killed his opponent. They then carried Ubaydah ؓ over to Rasulullah. Ubaydah's ؓ injuries were severe and he passed away at the feet of Rasulullah ﷺ. He was the first martyr of Badr.

[86] Abu Jahl was the Firown of this Ummah. However it has been said that his traits of arrogance and pride surpassed that of Firown. When Firown saw death coming he tried to embrace the true faith, whereas in his final moments Abu Jahl still continued to boast of his status and greatness.

[87] Rasulullah ﷺ had foretold that Umayyah bin Khalaf would be killed by the Sahabah. *See the introduction for the full narrative.*

[88] Seventy disbelievers were taken as captives.

The Aftermath of Badr

[89] Umm Fadl Lubabah ibn al-Harith ؓ was the wife of Abbas ibn Abdul Muttalib ؓ. She was furious that Abu Jahl hit her husband's freed slave, Abu

Rafi ﷺ, and that he was taking advantage of her husband's absence, who had been taken as a captive at Badr.

90 Safwan bin Umayyah ﷺ accepted Islam later on. He was the son of Umayyah bin Khalaf. Umayyah had been killed by the Muslims when Bilal ﷺ saw him as a captive of Abd ur-Rahman bin Awf ﷺ.

91 The deal that Safwan bin Umayyah ﷺ and Umair ibn Wahb ﷺ had struck had been kept private. Rasulullah ﷺ revealed his knowledge of the agreement Umair ﷺ had made with Safwan ibn Umayyah ﷺ and recounted the events that had led him to Madinah. Umair realised that Rasulullah ﷺ was a true messenger and thus embraced Islam. Rasulullah ﷺ instructed the Sahabah to teach Umair ﷺ about Islam and told them to free his captive.

However it is worth noting here that prior to this incident the disbelievers had witnessed many miracles at the hands of Rasulullah ﷺ. Why was it that at this juncture Umair ibn Wahb ﷺ accepted Islam? It is this author's humble opinion that together with the miracle of knowing of this private meeting, Umair ibn Wahb ﷺ was moved by the character, compassion and conduct of Rasulullah ﷺ. He was in his stronghold of Madinah, surrounded by loyal companions and had him subdued, an enemy who he knew intended to assassinate him. Any other king or leader in that position would have warranted such a man's arrest and ordered their execution, let alone allow that perpetrator to approach him with a poisoned blade. However Rasulullah ﷺ confronted him in an amicable and pleasant manner. Such sublime character would have overawed Umair ibn Wahb ﷺ and aided him in accepting Islam.

Muslims today need to realise the importance of good character as it is one of the most effective forms of da'wah.

91After the conquest of Makkah Safwan ibn Umayyah ﷺ fled. He feared the consequences of his actions and the recompense he would receive for the hatred and enmity he showed towards Islam. However Rasulullah ﷺ, who was the epitome of compassion, sent someone after him with a token of safe conduct. Safwan ﷺ returned and reconciled matters but he did not become a Muslim until after the Battle of Hunayn.

The Battle of Uhud

92 Rasulullah ﷺ wanted to fight the enemy on his own grounds, so that the Muslims could dictate the battlefield. However Abdullah bin Ubay who was a hypocrite and a coward wanted to stay in Madinah in order to avoid the war.

93 Many Sahabah who missed Badr made promises that they too would show their valour and courage at the next opportunity. When they were consulted as to where the battle should take place they wanted to meet the enemy on the

battlefield to prove true to their promise. They put their opinion forward very strongly, thus it was decided that they go out of Madinah to fight.

94 Rasulullah ﷺ had said he wanted to fight within Madinah but those Sahabah that had taken oaths to fight at the next opportunity strongly put forward their desire to leave Madinah and fight. Later those Sahabah resented not going according to the wish of Rasulullah ﷺ and asked for the decision to be changed.

95 Abdullah bin Ubay had planned with his fellow hypocrites to return before the battle. They did this to dishearten the Muslims and strike fear in them. The Muslims' numbers fell drastically due to the withdrawal of the hypocrites. Abdullah bin Ubay made an excuse that he had not agreed to leave Madinah to fight and they had gone against the opinion that he had put forward.

96 Rasulullah ﷺ placed these archers so that the enemy does not come around the hillock and attack them from the rear. The archers were posted to shoot down anyone who attempted to attack the Muslims from behind.

97 Zubair bin al-Awwam ﷺ was the son of Safiyyah bint Abdul Mutallib ﷺ, who was the aunt of Rasulullah ﷺ. This makes Zubair ﷺ the cousin of Rasulullah ﷺ. Notice how in both in Badr and Uhud it was Rasulullah's ﷺ relatives that rode out to fight the challengers.

98 Talhah bin Abi Talhah was so well known for his feats of bravery and skill that he was given the title 'the Battalion's Ram'.

99 The Muslims would attack the pagan flag bearer. When the flag bearer was killed another pagan would rush to their standard to avoid letting it fall. Every man who ran to uphold their flag was killed. This eludes towards how far into the ranks of the enemy the Muslims had penetrated.

100 Khalid bin Waleed ﷺ had not come into the fold of Islam yet.

101 They were not held liable nor will be sinful for their mistake. Those Muslims who died at another Muslim's hand will still be ranked amongst the martyrs.

102 Hamzah ibn Abdul Muttalib ﷺ was the uncle of Rasulullah ﷺ.

103 Hamzah ibn Abdul Muttalib ﷺwas given the honorific title of 'the Lion of Allah'.

104 Abu Ubaydah bin al-Jarrah ﷺ was given the title of 'the trustworthy one of this Ummah' by Rasulullah ﷺ.

105 When Rasulullah ﷺ was residing in Makkah he had said to Ubay bin Khalaf

that he would kill him. Ubay knew the truth in the words of Rasulullah ﷺ and was anxious to see Rasulullah ﷺ dead.

106 In spite of being a disbeliever contemplate on his faith in the words of Rasulullah ﷺ. He knew when Rasulullah ﷺ had said he would kill him that it would most definitely come true. To such an extent that he believed had Rasulullah ﷺ spat on him with the intention of it killing him, he would have died.

107 Hind ﷺ was the wife of Abu Sufyan ﷺ. She was the daughter of Utbah ibn Rabi'ah, the sister of Waleed ibn Utbah and the niece of Shaybah ibn Rabi'ah. All three of whom were killed at the beginning of the battle of Badr by Ali ﷺ, Hamzah ﷺ and Ubaydah bin al-Harith ﷺ. She was overjoyed at the martyrdom of Hamzah ﷺ and viewed it as revenge for her fallen family. She accepted Islam at the Conquest of Makkah. She played a vital role in the decisive Battle of Yarmuk which took place after the demise of Rasulullah ﷺ. The Muslims were greatly outnumbered and some would turn their backs to the battle. At this critical time Hind ﷺ and Asma bint Abi Bakr ﷺ would drive the Muslims back to the fight with their words and poetry.

108 Mus'ab bin Umair ﷺ was the Sahabi who had gone to Madinah to preach Islam prior to migration.

109 Hanzalah ﷺ had just left the bed of his wife and had not had the opportunity to bathe. He was given the title of Ghaseel ul-Malaikah, which means 'the one bathed by the angels'.

110 Hamzah ﷺ was of a close age to Rasulullah ﷺ. He was regarded as Rasulullah's ﷺ foster brother because they were both suckled by the same woman, Thuwaybah ﷺ, when they were children.

111 Safiyyah ﷺ was the aunt of Rasulullah ﷺ, the mother of Zubair bin al-Awwam ﷺ.

The Aftermath of Uhud

112 The battle of Uhud can be considered as a stalemate. Though the Muslims had retreated, the pagans had left the battlefield first. Rasulullah ﷺ was anxious about the plans of the disbelievers, he feared they may return.

113 Abdullah bin Ubay, the hypocrite, wanted to join the Muslims after having withdrawn the day before. But Rasulullah ﷺ had said that only those who had participated the day before were eligible to take part.

The Betrayal at ar-Raji

114 The relatives of the man who had been killed by Asim 🌟 wanted to mutilate his body to avenge the death of their family member.

115 The man who had been sent to retrieve Asim's 🌟 body was unable to do so as it was protected by a swarm of hornets.

116 Khubaib 🌟 was the first one to start the act of praying salaah before execution.

117 Khubaib 🌟 implied he would rather die than be sitting happily with his family whilst Rasulullah 🌟 was being pricked by a thorn. In other words he would happily die, foregoing all the pleasure of the world and the company of his family, if it meant he could save Rasulullah 🌟 from the pricking of a thorn.

Massacre at Ma'una

118 Rasulullah 🌟 had told the Sahabah that on their route to Najd they should pass his message on to Amir bin Tufail when they come across his place of residence.

119 Abu Bara did not want the bloodshed, he had promised to protect the Sahabah. Due to his protection Banu Amir did not respond to their leader's call. Amir then got his assistance from Banu Sulaym.

120 The Muslims were unaware of what had happened to Haram bin Milhan 🌟. They did not know that Amir had gathered the Banu Sulaym and they were unprepared to defend themselves. The one Sahabi that remained was Ka'b ibn Zaid 🌟 who was severely wounded and left for dead.

121 Two Sahabah were told to look after their animals of transportation. They had taken them away from the other Sahabah. When they saw birds circling overhead they realised that the Muslims had been betrayed and a fight was ongoing. They rushed to the battlefield to share in the reward and assist their fellow Muslims.

122 Amir's mother had taken a pledge to emancipate a slave. Amir took this opportunity to fulfil that pledge and freed Amr bin Umayyah 🌟.

123 Fajr Salaah is the prayer before sunrise.

The Expulsion of Banu Nadeer

124 After Rasulullah's 🌟 arrival to Madinah the Jews had signed a treaty with the Muslims.

¹²⁵ Huyay bin Akhtab was the chief of Banu Nadeer.

The Battle of al-Ahzab

¹²⁶ Observe the strength of the faith of the Sahabah. In such dire circumstances when the Muslims were finding it difficult to defend their own homes and were worried about protecting Madinah they were being promised victory over the lands of the greatest empires of the time. At a time when people would question their own survival, the Sahabah readily accepted the words of Rasulullah ﷺ as true.

¹²⁷ We can understand the physical prowess and valour of these men by the fact that three of them were willing to come and face three thousand Muslims. They were considered amongst the bravest of men, who were equal to a thousand men. Amr ibn Abd Wudd waved his sword and bellowed, "Is there any challenger?" Ali ؓ was the first to volunteer however Rasulullah ﷺ deemed him too inexperienced to go against such a veteran who was renowned for his strength, brute force and skill. Again Ali ؓ put himself forward but Rasulullah ﷺ felt a more senior Sahabi was better suited. When Ali ؓ showed his insistence for a third time Rasulullah ﷺ dispatched Ali ؓ, his son-in-law. Amr ibn Abd Wudd dismounted from his horse and struck off its head and legs implying he did not need a horse to face a mere child. It is stated that Ali ؓ killed him with a single strike of his sword. He pierced his armour and severed his neck and his jaw. Ikramah and Dirar fled when they saw how easily Ali ؓ had felled the giant, Amr.

¹²⁸ Asr is the salaah that is prayed late in the afternoon.

¹²⁹ Notice how Rasulullah ﷺ did not invoke the wrath of Allah upon the people of Ta'if when the Angel of the Mountains asked if he should crush the people who had chased him out of the city whilst hailing stones on him. Also during the Battle of Uhud Rasulullah ﷺ was continuously praying to Allah to forgive the disbelievers. However at this juncture Rasulullah ﷺ has invoked Allah's wrath upon them not due to the difficulty and constraint the Confederates had put upon them, not because of the siege they had laid upon Madinah but due to missing salaah because of them. This incident shows us how important salaah is and how much remorse one should feel at praying a salaah when its time has passed. Now reflect on our condition, how lightly do we take it when we miss a salaah? Let alone feeling remorse after praying it after its time has passed, we don't even feel ashamed that we don't read it at all.

¹³⁰ Ka'b bin Asad was the chief of Banu Qurayzah. Huyay bin Akhtab was the chief of Banu Nadeer who had been exiled from Madinah. They had settled in the stronghold of Khaybar.

[131] The hypocrites excused themselves saying their homes were vulnerable. The real reason they withdrew was to try and strike fear into the Muslims, in order to make them feel their numbers were dwindling.

[132] Prior to the Muslims of Madinah being unified as the Ansaar, they were divided into two main factions, Banu Aws and Banu Khazraj. There was much rivalry and fighting between them but through Islam their hearts were united. Sa'd bin Mu'adh ﷺ was the leader of the Banu Aws whilst Sa'd bin Ubadah ﷺ was the leader of Banu Khazraj.

[133] Sa'd bin Mu'adh's ﷺ wounds were fatal. He prayed to Allah to keep him alive if there was going to be any more battles with the pagans of Makkah. He also prayed to be kept alive until retribution was taken against Banu Qurayzah.

[134] Nu'aym bin Masood ﷺ kept his faith hidden. He went as a well-wisher to Banu Qurayzah and told them to ask for hostages from the Quraish. He reasoned with them that if the Quraish decided to flee from the battle then Banu Qurayzah would be defenceless against the Muslims. Whereas if they had Quraishi hostages the Quraish would not readily leave the battle out of fear of what would happen to their relatives who had been given as hostages to Banu Qurayzah.

[134] On the other hand Nu'aym ﷺ told the Quraish that Banu Qurayzah regretted their betrayal of the Muslims. They had therefore struck a deal with them that they would hand over Quraishi hostages to them in order to be forgiven. He advised the Quraish not to surrender any of their men as hostages.

[134] Banu Qurayzah saw the wisdom in Nu'aym's ﷺ words and went and asked for hostages from the Quraish. The Quraish thought that what Nu'aym ﷺ had told them was true, so they refused to hand over hostages. This caused great dissension amongst them which worked to the advantage of the Muslims.

The Siege of Banu Qurayzah

[135] Jews consider the Sabbath, which is a Saturday, as a day of rest. Attacking the Muslims on this day would have taken the Muslims by surprise as they would not have expected the Jews to go against their religion and attack on their day of rest.

[136] Abu Lubabah ﷺ had accidently told the Jews what Rasulullah ﷺ had decided for them.

[137] Banu Qurayzah had been allies with Banu Aws prior to Islam. They expected to be shown mercy and leniency from them. So they agreed to surrender on the condition that Sa'd bin Mu'adh ﷺ, the leader of Banu Aws, would pass the verdict on what should be done to them.

138 Sa'd bin Mu'adh 🙵 had prayed to Allah to keep him alive until revenge was taken against Banu Qurayzah. This had been done. He had also prayed to be allowed to live if any more fighting against the pagans of Makkah was going to occur. This was also accepted. The pagans did not attack the Muslims after the battle of the trenches. The Muslims conquered Makkah peacefully.

The Treaty of Hudaybiyah

139 In the state of ihram a Muslim is forbidden to do specific things, from amongst these fighting and quarrelling is strictly prohibited. They had donned the two pieces of cloth which are worn in the state of ihram, this was a sure sign they had come in peace.

140 Urwah ibn Masood 🙵 had been sent by the Quraish to observe the Muslims. He embraced Islam at a later date.

141 The Muslims did not need to fight as it was later verified that the rumours were false. 'Bay'at ur-Ridwan' means 'the pledge of pleasure', named thus due to Allah being pleased with the pledge.

142 The Muslims could not attack any tribe that had allied themselves with the Quraish. Similarly the Quraish could not attack any tribe that had allied itself with the Muslims.

143 The first verse of Surah Fat'h states, "Verily we have granted you (O Muhammad 🙵) a manifest victory'.

Propagating Islam

144 Rasulullah 🙵 was unlettered. The wisdom behind this is that it is not possible for an unread man to be able to invent a book as eloquent and full of knowledge as the Qur'an. This was proof that the Qur'an was indeed from Allah. Rasulullah 🙵 had no teacher other than Allah. Therefore he could not be accused of having learnt the content of the Qur'an from someone else.

The Conquest of Khaybar

145 By marrying Rasulullah 🙵, Safiyyah 🙵 became one of 'the mothers of the believers'.

146 Aa'isha 🙵 narrates that the Messenger 🙵, in the illness from which he passed away, used to say, "O Aa'isha, I still feel the pain caused by the food I ate at Khaybar. At this time I feel as though my aorta is being cut from that poison."

The Campaign of Mu'tah

147 This was Zaid bin Haritha 🙵 who had been adopted by Rasulullah 🙵.

¹⁴⁸ Khalid bin Waleed ﷺ was a great military general and tactician. By reshuffling the flanks he gave the impression that fresh troops had arrived. Such a small group of Muslims were holding against such a large force, so the Romans were gravely concerned that fresh troops would tip the balance in the favour of the Muslims.

¹⁴⁹ The Romans feared reinforcements had arrived. They thought that the Muslims were drawing them out to be ambushed by a hidden platoon. In this manner Khalid bin Waleed ﷺ was able to withdraw the army to safety.

The Conquest of Makkah

¹⁵⁰ One of the terms of the treaty was that the Muslims could not attack the allies of the Quraish, nor could the Quraish attack the allies of the Muslims. The Quraish had broken the treaty by assisting Banu Bakr in their attack against the Banu Khuza'ah, who had allied themselves with the Muslims.

¹⁵¹ The Quraish did not agree with any of the three options. They sent Abu Sufyan ﷺ to try and convince Rasulullah ﷺ to renew the treaty and overlook the incident.

¹⁵² Abbas ibn Abdul Muttalib ﷺ had accepted Islam and was emigrating to Madinah. He came across the Muslims who were advancing upon Madinah. When Rasulullah ﷺ named him the last Muhajir (emigrant) he foretold the upcoming victory. Makkah was going to be subdued. Therefore there was no need to emigrate from Makkah to Madinah. This made Abbas ibn Abdul Muttalib ﷺ the last Muhajir.

The Battle of Hunayn

¹⁵³ The Muslims felt sure of victory when they saw their strength in their numbers. Allah was displeased that they were looking towards their strength in numbers and not their strength in faith. He caused the Muslims to flee from the battle when they were taken unaware in order to teach them that Allah has control over everything, one should put their faith solely in Allah.

¹⁵⁴ This was Abu Sufyan ibn al-Haarith ibn Abdul Muttalib ﷺ. Thus he was the paternal cousin of Rasulullah ﷺ. He is not to be confused with Abu Sufyan ibn Harb ﷺ, who was the father-in-law of Rasulullah ﷺ, as Rasulullah ﷺ was married to his daughter, Umm Habibah ﷺ.

Hawazin Accept Islam

¹⁵⁵ Observe how the Sahabah did not say that they too are returning their share of the booty to the people of Hawazin. Rather they made it the property of

Rasulullah ﷺ, who had promised to return whatever was his back to the Hawazin. They wanted the honour of also having their property returned by Rasulullah ﷺ.

156 Halimah ﵁ was the lady who had nursed Rasulullah ﷺ as a child. Her daughter was Sheyma ﵁, who was amongst the captives.

The Expedition of Tabuk

157 Some Sahabah were unable to go due to an illness, whilst some poor Sahabah wanted to go but could not be accommodated for. The three Sahabah mentioned here were healthy and had the provisions to be able to go but they still remained behind. One of them was Ka'b ibn Malik ﵁. Upon the return of the army the hypocrites made excuses to Rasulullah ﷺ of their inability to participate. However Ka'b ibn Malik ﵁ and two other Sahabah confessed that they had no excuse for staying behind. Rasulullah ﷺ told them to leave the gathering until Allah reveals what should be done with them. The three Sahabah were boycotted. Nobody was allowed to talk to them, not even their family members. Life became very difficult and unbearable for them and they felt constrained. After fifty days Allah revealed verses which consisted of their forgiveness. Their honesty saved them from their sins and ensured their forgiveness, whereas those who lied, though they got away with it in this world, they will be reckoned for it in the hereafter.

157 In Surah Tawbah Allah mentions their forgiveness, *"And to the three who were left behind until the earth became narrow despite its vastness and their souls confined them and they were certain there is no refuge from Allah except in Him, then He turned to them so they could repent, indeed Allah is the Acceptor of Repentance, the Merciful."* After this verse Allah points out the beautiful moral character of these three Sahabah, *"O you who have believed, fear Allah and be with those who are truthful."*

157 Due to their honesty, love for Allah and fear of accountability in the hereafter they owned up. Allah honoured them by mentioning their forgiveness in the Qur'an, which has been recited since that day and is still recited by Muslims today. He also praises their integrity by telling believers to stay with those who are truthful. We also need to inculcate a fear of Allah and create a realisation of our accountability in the hereafter. This will enable us to accept our wrongdoings, repent and turn to Allah for forgiveness.

158 This was another great test. Despite their indescribable hunger and thirst the Sahabah readily accepted the command of Allah and did not drink from the well nor did they eat the dough that contained its water.

رَبَّنَا تَقَبَّلْ مِنَّا إِنَّكَ أَنْتَ السَّمِيعُ العَلِيم

"O our Lord! Accept (this service) from us: For Thou art the All-Hearing, the All-knowing."